A "Hands On"
approach to teaching...

Measurement

Grades 3 - 8

Andy Heidemann

Natalie Hernandez

Jeanette Lenger

Ron Long

Petti Pfau

Scott Purdy

Sharon Rodgers

Linda Sue Brisby

HANDS ON, INC.   **SOLVANG, CALIFORNIA**

Layout and Graphics: Scott Purdy
Cover Art: Petti Pfau
Illustrations: Petti Pfau, Suzi Matthies, Scott Purdy

Order Number: HO 102 - I (Intermediate)
ISBN 0 - 927726 - 09 - 2

HANDS ON, INC.
2121 Rebild Drive
Solvang, CA 93463

Introduction

This book was compiled by a group of kindergarten through eighth grade teachers at Solvang Elementary School in Solvang, California. It is one of a series of seven books we have written with the purpose of filling a void which we were experiencing at our school, and which we anticipated was being experienced at many other schools as well.

In 1985, the State of California released a document entitled **Mathematics Framework For California Public Schools.** The document was revolutionary in that it sought to restructure the process of teaching math in the classroom. State commitment was so strong that all textbooks submitted for state adoption were initially rejected by the state textbook committee.

Six years later, as we release the second edition of our books, a new state Framework is being readied which re-emphasizes and expands upon the stand taken by the original Framework document. Math strands, domains, manipulatives, problem solving, cooperative learning, and calculators are "IN" (emphasized). Algorithms, memorization, pencil and paper math, and standardized tests are "OUT" (de-emphasized)!

At Solvang School we had been involved in a "hands-on"approach to teaching math for a number of years. Still, we were caught in the situation of wondering how to apply the directions of the original Framework. From this uncertainty came the beginnings of Hands On math books which are an invaluable supplement to your mathematics program.

All lessons described in this book are activity based. We feel strongly that children learn best when they have concrete experiences in learning mathematical concepts.

Our approach is to provide a TASK ANALYSIS of the skills children need to understand MEASUREMENT, and to give a variety of activities which allow children to learn these skills. Activities are organized from basic to complex within each task analysis item and each lesson has a list of necessary materials, recommended classroom organization, and a basic explanation of the lesson format. We have also included extensions of many lessons along with numerous experiences in teaching the metric system.

This book was written BY TEACHERS FOR TEACHERS, and we use these activities in our classrooms every day. All activities involve the use of easily obtainable and inexpensive objects as manipulatives. There is no need to spend large sums of money to teach math. We also feel that this approach enhances the "real world" applications of our lessons. We have left out the typical flow charts, color coding, and cross reference pages that often accompany multi-grade level texts. We have included only practical, teacher based information that you can read once and use.

What we have provided is organized, concise, activity oriented lessons for teaching MEASUREMENT to third through eighth grade children. We have included this wide grade span to allow you to choose activities which fit the needs of students who need enrichment and remediation as well as the students who are working at grade level.

TASK ANALYSIS

Primary

Time - Calendar	P1. Locates and reads the days of the week on the calendar and is able to read and find given dates and days.	Primary
Time - Calendar	P2. States and orders the months and the number of days in each month.	Primary
Time - Clock	P3. Identifies hour and minute (hands/symbols) on both a standard and digital clock and is able to set time to the hour, half-hour,and quarter hour.	Primary
Money	P4. Identifies a penny, nickel, and dime and states their respective value.	Primary
Money	P5. Counts to a given monetary amount using coins of the same and of mixed denominations.	Primary
Money	P6. Makes change using pennies, nickels, and dimes.	Primary
Perimeter	P7. Develops the concept of perimeter.	Primary
Linear Measure	P8. Estimates and counts units of length and establishes need for standard units of measure.	Primary
Area	P9. Builds and counts the number of square units inside a figure.	Primary
Area	P10. Compares the size and area of various shapes.	Primary
Weight	P11. Weighs and compares the weight of two simple objects using arbitrary units of measure.	Primary
Volume	P12. Uses arbitrary units to make an estimate, and measurement, and an order for the volume of various containers.	Primary
Liquid Measure	P13. Measures amounts in pints, quarts, and gallons.	Primary

Grades 3 - 8

Time - Clock	1. Configures hour and minute hands to five minute settings and counts by fives to sixty.	Middle
Time - Clock	2. Sets clock to writes in conventional notation to one minute intervals.	Middle
Time - Clock	3. States time equivalency and patterns for seconds, minutes, hours, days, weeks, months, years, decades, and centuries.	Middle/Upper
Time - Clock	4. Identifies AM/PM and time zone relationships and purposes.	Upper
Time - Clock	5. Uses a stop watch and can read time to the 10th of a second.	Upper
Money	6. Counts to a monetary value using coins of mixed value.	Middle

Money	7. Makes change using pennies, nickels, dimes, and quarters.	Middle
Money	8. Identifies quarters half-dollars, and dollars, and states their respective and equivalent values.	Middle
Money	9. Identifies and writes value for a given amount using dollar signs and decimal places.	Middle
Money	10. Adds and subtracts (makes change for) money value up to four digits.	Middle
Money	11. Multiplies and divides monetary amounts by whole numbers.	Upper
Linear Measure	12. Compares, estimates, and measures length (height) in inches, feet, yards, and metric measures.	Middle
Perimeter	13. Measures and computes perimeter in standard and in metric units.	Middle
Linear Measure	14. Converts standard measures of inches, feet, and yards into equivalent values.	Middle/Upper
Linear Measure	15. Identifies and measures the parts of a circle (circumference, arc, etc.).	Middle/Upper
Linear Measure	16. Identifies meaning of milli, centi, deci, hecto, kilo, and shows equivalencies.	Middle/Upper
Area	17. Differentiates between area and perimeter.	Middle
Area	18. Determines and uses formulas to measure the area of various shapes.	Upper
Area	19. Develops an understanding of the meaning of "pi" in using formulas to find the area and circumference of a circle.	Upper
Area	20. Computes surface area of solids.	Upper
Weight	21. Identifies ounces, pounds, and tons (grams, kilograms) as standard units of measure and uses them to estimate and compare weights of various objects.	Middle
Weight	22. Identifies equivalencies of weight Including ounces, pounds, and tons (grams and kilograms).	Middle
Volume	23. Identifies the properties of a cube and constructs shapes using cubes.	Middle
Volume	24. Counts number of cubic units in a given figure and constructs figures to find specific volume.	Middle
Volume	25. Differentiates between surface area and volume.	Upper
Volume	26. Computes and identifies properties and formulas to determine the volume of various three dimensional shapes.	Upper
Liquid Measure	27. Estimates the size of various containers and measures equivalent units among cups, pints, quarts, and gallons (liters, milliliters).	Middle/Upper

Table of Contents

Measurement

1	**Configures Hour and Minute Hands to Five Minute Settings and Counts by Fives to Sixty**

Stick Around

Grade Level: Middle

MATERIALS: Tongue depressors or ice cream sticks (12 per group)

ORGANIZATION: Teams of three or four children

PROCEDURE: In this activity, students will be visualizing the position of clock hands and relating these positions to numbers of minutes.

Begin by drawing a clock on the chalkboard or overhead and ask students to brainstorm different things they know about a clock — accept all responses. Hand out ice cream sticks to each group and tell students that they are going to create a clock with twelve minute hands — NO HOUR HAND.

Have them arrange the 12 sticks in a neat array. Let them experiment with the formation, but eventually, students will arrive upon a daisy type pattern as shown below.

Ask students if they know how many minutes are represented by each ice cream stick (5) and let them count by fives to discover the number of minutes in an hour. Next, have students remove one of the sticks and ask how many minutes are represented by the newly created space (10). Have them remove another stick and ask for that minute representation (15).

Let students play a game among group members of removing consecutive ice cream sticks and then identifying the number of minutes represented by the space.

The purpose of this activity is to get students to begin to understand the shape of a quarter clock being 15 minutes, a third of a clock being 20 minutes, etc. The students will also be practicing counting by fives.

Hands On, Inc
2121 Rebild Drive
Solvang, CA 93463

1	**Configures Hour and Minute Hands to Five Minute Settings and Counts by Fives to Sixty**

The Art of Clock Making
Grade Level: Middle

MATERIALS: Paper plates, brass fasteners, scissors, tagboard or posterboard, and markers

ORGANIZATION: To be done individually or in teams of two students

PROCEDURE: This is a project which is already done in many classrooms each year. We feel it is important for children to create a clockface and, so we have included it here.

Give each student a paper plate, tagboard, and a brass fastener. They should make pencil marks at the appropriate places on the clockface for 1-12 clock intervals.

Have them design an hour hand and a minute hand keeping in mind that the hour hand is shorter (they can remember this easily by associating the length of the hand to the length of the word). Punch a hole in the tail end of the hands and in the center of the paper plate. Next, they attach the hands with the brass fastener (brad) and ensure that hands move freely.

Students can leave these clocks on top of their desks and each time you have a few minutes for a transition or sponge activity, use the clocks for practice.

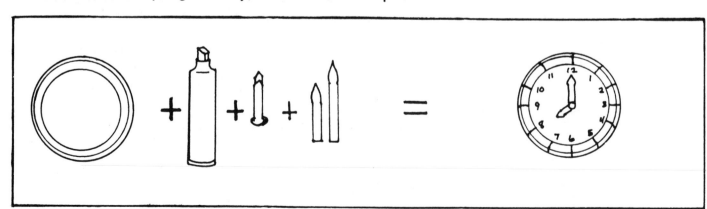

Hands On, Inc
2121 Rebild Drive
Solvang, CA 93463

1	## Configures Hour and Minute Hands to Five Minute Settings and Counts by Fives to Sixty

The Mouse Runs 'Round the Clock

Grade Level: Middle

MATERIALS: No special materials are necessary for this activity

ORGANIZATION: A whole class activity

PROCEDURE: This lesson is a combination physical education/math lesson in which students make a human clock.

To prepare students for the activity, draw a clock on the chalkboard and tell the students that they will be forming a large clock on the playground and will move to various times as a group. The class will form the circle, one student will be the minute hand, and one student the hour hand. You can also use a group of students for the minute and hour hands.

There are several approaches you can use with this idea:

Game One: Blow a whistle once for go, twice for stop. When students "go" the minute hand walks forward (around) and the hour hand moves slowly around so that the minute hand hits 12 just as the hour hand hits the correct hour. Students have a lot of fun in the "crossover" — when the minute hand passes the hour hand.

7:00

Game Two,: Once students have formed the clock, say a time (1:35) and let the "hands" move to that time; if they are correct, they get to show another time, if they are incorrect, the hands and two of the circle children switch places.

Game Three: Involve the circle group by having 12:00 switch positions each time a new time is given. This is done by designating a different student at 12:00 each time.

Hands On, Inc
2121 Rebild Drive
Solvang, CA 93463

1	**Configures Hour and Minute Hands to Five Minute Settings and Counts by Fives to Sixty**

Time on My Hands
Grade Level: Middle

MATERIALS: No special materials are necessary

ORGANIZATION: Teams of two, three, or four students

PROCEDURE: This exercise provides practice in counting by fives and then translates the student's hand "height" to time.

Begin by telling students that they have something in common with a clock. A clock can count by fives and their hands (fingers) count by fives. You can also include the idea of measuring horses with hands rather than with standard feet and inches.

Tell students that they will be measuring one another with their hands, but that these hands will then become like the hands of a clock to convert everyone's height into time. Give each group time to measure one another by hands. If some students end up with 27 and 1/2 hands, that will add to the overall effectiveness of the lesson.

To convert hand height to time, begin with 12:00. Since each hand has five fingers, each hand will represent five minutes on the clock; therefore, 12 hands would represent 60 minutes or one hour —making the time 1:00.

A student who was 27 and 1/2 hands high would be 2:17 or 2:18. It sounds confusing but if the teacher goes through the procedure with the entire class saying, "One hand - 12:05, Two hands - 12:10," etc. student will get the concept and have fun reciting their five-facts and learning about the movement of a clock.

As an extension, you can have students measure various things in the room and convert these measurements to time or have students state their height in minutes or hours and minutes (180 minutes or 2 1/2 hours tall).

Hands On, Inc
2121 Rebild Drive
Solvang, CA 93463

| 2 | # Sets Clock and Writes in Conventional Notation to One Minute Intervals |

A Handy Clockface

Grade Level: Middle

MATERIALS: Butcher paper, tempera paint, clean up area, and shallow pie tins or sponge

ORGANIZATION: In teams of two students so they can help one another

PROCEDURE: This is a combination art/math lesson in which students will be creating a "clock" with hand prints.

Begin by drawing a clockface on the board and discussing the organization of the clock — each number representing five minutes. Ask students to notice that they too have a measure of five minutes, their hands!

Tell students that they are going to create a personalized clock which not only shows the five minute intervals but also each individual minute (fingers). They will do this by dipping their hands in paint and then forming a circle with hand prints. Before beginning to dip their hands in paint, they will need to plan for the size of the circle. Let each team work out its own strategy.

When they actually begin dipping their hands (a shallow pie tin barely covered with poster paint works well), you may want to let each child dip one hand in one color and the other hand in another, or have one team member be one color and the other team member be a second color. Alternating colors provides an even more vivid depiction of the five minute clock groupings.

You will probably find that most groups will produce a very lopsided clock on the first try, so we suggest that you let them do a second clock before cleaning up.

Once students have finished their clock faces, you can do many activities with these "posters."

Hands On, Inc
2121 Rebild Drive
Solvang, CA 93463

2	# Sets Clock and Writes in Conventional Notation to One Minute Intervals

"Walk" Around the Clock
Grade Level: Middle

MATERIALS: Chalk, a large asphalt or concrete area for students

ORGANIZATION: Individually or in teams of two students

PROCEDURE: In this activity, each student or team will be drawing a large clock on the playground surface and then will walk to display a time given by the teacher or another student.

Begin the activity in the room by drawing a clock on the chalkboard. Include the marks for minutes as well as the 1 to 12 numeration. Tell students that they will be drawing their own clockfaces on the school playground with chalk and will then use the minute markers to play a game.

Give each student or team time to draw a circle (large enough for a small step to be equal to one minute), place numbers and then make the one minute marks. These marks should be at least a small step apart. Have students mark the five minute marks (at each number) with a heavier chalk line.

Once the drawing is complete, have students stand at 12:00. Tell them to walk five minutes, five more minutes, ten more minutes, etc. When they have reached different points on the clock (1/4, 1/3, 1/2, 2/3) ask them to tell how many "minutes" they have walked.

As an extension, have two students stand on each clock — one being the minute hand, and one the hour hand. As a team, let them form various times which the teacher calls out.

Hands On, Inc
2121 Rebild Drive
Solvang, CA 93463

2	**Sets Clock and Writes in Conventional Notation to One Minute Intervals**

Eraser at 12:00 O'clock High

Grade Level: Middle

MATERIALS: No special materials are necessary for this lesson.

ORGANIZATION: A whole class activity

PROCEDURE: Begin by asking students if they know how airplane pilots know what direction they are heading. Students will generate discussion regarding north, south, etc.

Tell students that there is another way that pilots talk about their directions. They use the numbers on an imaginary clock to describe their bearings. Demonstrate this by making the front of the classroom 12:00 o'clock. Then have students identify objects in the room that would be at 3:00, 6:00, etc.

Once students understand the concept, ask one of the children to come forward and secretly select an item in the room. Using the "clock directions," have the student describe the location of a selected item with a statement such as, "I see something red at 4:00 o'clock." The student can then select a classmate to identify the item.

Extend the lesson by using minute locations such as, "I see something blue at 43 minutes." These conversions are very helpful in having students become familiar with a clockface. To vary the game, you can change the direction of 12:00 o'clock with each new player.

2	**Sets Clock and Writes in Conventional Notation to One Minute Intervals**

Round and Round We Go!
Grade Level: Middle

MATERIALS: Construction paper, markers

ORGANIZATION: A whole class activity

PROCEDURE: This is a fun activity which demonstrates the workings of a digital clock combined with the process of telling time.

Do a brief discussion of how a digital clock operates — for these purposes it is best to explain that some digital clocks work like an odometer in a car. All numbers 0 - 9 are on a cylinder and as the cylinder revolves, different number appear. Each time the ones column cylinder completes a revolution, it triggers the tens column cylinder to move one turn, etc.

Students will have fun mimicking this movement. Select ten students to be the minutes - ones column; ten students to be the minutes - tens column; and ten students to be the hours - hundreds column. If you have fewer than thirty children, eliminate the higher numbers for hours.

Have each child select a number (0-9) to color on his/her construction paper. Have students form a circle and practice the motion of rotating and then changing the next column.

You might even want to perform this "clock" for other classes. As an extra activity, let other class members call out a time and let the clock move to display this time.

Students can also make individual digital clocks by writing numbers around a series of paper towel rolls and then turning the rolls to simulate the movement inside a clock.

Hands On, Inc
2121 Rebild Drive
Solvang, CA 93463

3	**States Time Equivalency and Patterns for Seconds, Minutes, Hours, Days, Weeks, Months, Years, Decades, and Centuries**

Second Guessing

Grade Level: Middle/Upper

MATERIALS: Calculators, tally sheets (as below)

ORGANIZATION: Individually or in pairs, to allow students to help one another.

PROCEDURE: In this lesson students will try to calculate the number of months, weeks, days, hours, and minutes (seconds) which they have been alive. The real goal is for students to work with equivalent amounts of time, but there are side benefits in using calculator and tally sheets.

Begin the lesson by asking each student to write his/her birthdate in the proper square. From this information they can decide upon the best way to approach the problem. Let students struggle with the approach before giving them help. They should all have sufficient familiarity with the calendar to be able to figure out an approach. Have students who are unsure of actual time of birth to pick an arbitrary time of birth.

You can extend the lesson by tallying the total number of seconds the whole class has been alive. This information can then be worked backwards by division to minutes, hours, days, etc.

Birthdate				
years	months	days	hours	minutes

Hands On, Inc
2121 Rebild Drive
Solvang, CA 93463

3	States Time Equivalency and Patterns for Seconds, Minutes, Hours, Days, Weeks, Months, Years, Decades, and Centuries

Scavengers for Time
Grade Level: Middle/Upper

MATERIALS: No special materials are necessary for this lesson

ORGANIZATION: Teams of three or four students

PROCEDURE: This activity requires students to list items around the school. The catch is that each item collected must represent a time frame that is best measured in a particular time segment, a second, a minute, an hour, a day, a week, a year, or a century.

Begin the lesson by discussing with students the various time structures. They all know the items listed below. Ask students to give examples of items whose age is best measured in seconds. Examples might include a leaf falling from a tree, tying a shoe, or a door closing. Continue by discussing items which might be measured in minutes, hours, weeks, etc.

Tell students that they will be going on a scavenger hunt and they must list one item or idea which represents each one of these time frames. Some possible items include:

> seconds: the sound of a school bell,
> minutes: a cup of coffee, a lunch, notebook paper
> hours: chalk marks on the playground
> weeks: a pencil or pen,
> years: a school desk, chair, a notebook, play equipment
> decades: a school building
> centuries: trees at school,

When students have returned to class, post or display the items and discuss. You may want to extend this to find equivalent values. For example, "How many pencils do you use in a school year?" "How many sheets of paper do you use in a week?" "If a school building stands for 40 years, how many students will attend school?" All of these questions lead students to an understanding of the relationship of time periods..

Hands On, Inc
2121 Rebild Drive
Solvang, CA 93463

3	**States Time Equivalency and Patterns for Seconds, Minutes, Hours, Days, Weeks, Months, Years, Decades, and Centuries**

Patterning Your Years

Grade Level: Middle/Upper

MATERIALS: A perpetual calendar for each student (Appendix E)

ORGANIZATION: Individually or in pairs, to allow students to help one another.

PROCEDURE: This is a fun activity in which students will figure the day of the week on which they were born, and the day of the week on which their birthday has fallen for each year. The purpose of the lesson is for students to find a pattern of days and the effect of leap year upon this pattern. Younger students will have to go to future birthdays in order to find the pattern.

Demonstrate the use of a perpetual calendar for the students, and tell them what their goal in completing this lesson will be. Most adults are aware that our 365 day calendar divided by 7 days per week leaves a remainder of one — meaning that a Tuesday, January 1 in 1987 will be followed by a Wednesday, January 1 in 1988. Students have not realized this pattern and it should be an interesting basic concept. Do not, however, tell students that this pattern exists; let them have the fun of making this discovery.

Prepare a blank tally sheet (completed sheet shown) for each of the students. After they have compiled information let students share their tally sheets with one another to solidify the premise of the lesson. You might also include a discussion as to why leap year is necessary and how students can remember when leap year falls (every four years).

YEAR	DAY OF WEEK
1976	Wednesday
1977	Thursday
1978	Friday
1979	Saturday
1980	Monday
1981	Tuesday
1982	Wednesday
1983	Thursday
1984	Saturday
1985	Sunday
1986	Monday
1987	Tuesday
1988	Thursday

Hands On, Inc
2121 Rebild Drive
Solvang, CA 93463

3	**States Time Equivalency and Patterns for Seconds, Minutes, Hours, Days, Weeks, Months, Years, Decades, and Centuries**

Moon Magic
Grade Level: Middle/Upper

MATERIALS: A calendar of the year for each student, blank calendars as in Appendix F (an almanac is very useful)

ORGANIZATION: Groups of two, three, or four students

PROCEDURE: Give each student a calendar for the current year and ask why the calendar is set up as it is and the basis upon which it is structured (the movement of the sun). Have them list the benefits of the calendar as it is.

Ask students to discuss what would happen if the calendar were based upon the movement of the moon rather than the movement of the sun. What impact would this have?

Basic facts you will need to cover include the 29 1/2 day cycle of the moon, the phases of the moon, and fact that the moon does not appear every day at the same time (which the sun does to a degree). Based on this discussion, have students create a year-long calendar which is based upon the movement of the moon.

Some students will simply write in new dates, but you will find that some class members will really begin to be curious about the effects of such a change. Encourage them to talk with their parents about the effects. Using the enthusiasm of this group of interested students, have the entire class prepare a chart or report identifying the benefits and drawbacks of the solar and lunar calendars.

As an extension have students do a report on the Chinese and Vietnamese lunar calendars. These calendars use 12 months of 29 to 30 days in a sixty year cycle which is divided into 12 year epochs. Each year is named after an animal.

First Lunar Month: ZOLTAN

Onesday	Twosday	Threesday	Foursday	Fivesday
1	2	3	4	5
6	7	8	9	10
11	12	13	14	15
16	17	18	19	20
26	27	28	29	30

Hands On, Inc
2121 Rebild Drive
Solvang, CA 93463

4	**Identifies AM/PM and Time Zone Relationships and Purposes**

A-peel-ing Time

Grade Level: Upper

MATERIALS: Various types of sectioned fruit (oranges, grapefruit, tangerines)

ORGANIZATION: Teams of two, three, or four students

PROCEDURE: Have students peel the skin off of the fruit and divide the fruit into sections. Tell students that they are going to decide how to divide the sections into "time zones."

Begin by asking students to discuss the number of time zones recognized on earth (twenty-four). Discuss why this has been done this way and ask them to create some alternatives to this arrangement. Examples might include twelve two hour time zones, or eight three-hour zones, etc. Discuss the benefits of such arrangements.

You might want to have students do measurements of the distance around the equator and divide this figure by twenty-four to find the number of miles in each   time zone. You may find the world map in Appendix H is helpful in this lesson.

Now have students use their fruit sections as time zones (dividing 24 hours by the number of sections). Students should write a paragraph explaining the amount of time in each zone, and the difficulties and benefits of such an arrangement.

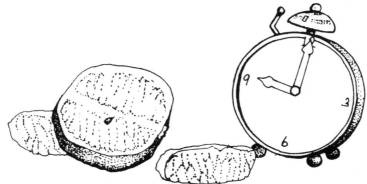

 Hands On, Inc
2121 Rebild Drive
Solvang, CA 93463

4	**Identifies AM/PM and Time Zone Relationships and Purposes**

Finding Your Comfort Zone
Grade Level: Upper

MATERIALS: Magazines (especially National Geographic), scissors, a world map with time zones (see Appendix H).

ORGANIZATION: To be done individually or in groups of two, three, or four students.

PROCEDURE: This is a very effective activity which can be used in coordination with a social studies lesson on world cultures. Explain the concept of time zones and the need for these zones (use previous time zone lesson).

Each group of students should select a different time of day for the time zone in which they live and find a picture which represents what people do at this time of the day. As they move around the world, they should try to find pictures which show the activities of various cultures at different points of the world at the same moment of the day (i.e., breakfast, working, dinner, nightlife, sleeping, etc.). Students then paste these pictures at the appropriate places on the map and label with the correct time.

When students have finished with their maps, they can be used as displays, providing several opportunities for writing and discussion activities.

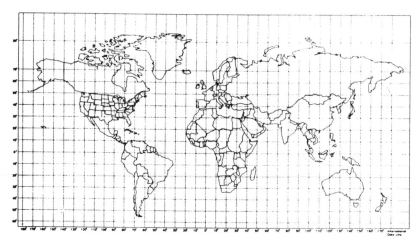

Hands On, Inc
2121 Rebild Drive
Solvang, CA 93463

<table>
<tr><td>**4**</td><td>**Identifies AM/PM and Time Zone Relationships and Purposes**</td></tr>
</table>

Staff of Ra

Grade Level: Upper

MATERIALS: A stick or staff of some type, a school wall which can be marked on, markers or paint, and a carpenter's level.

ORGANIZATION: A whole class activity

PROCEDURE: This is an ongoing or year-long exercise in which students will mark the location of the sun at 9 am and 3 pm to track the movement of the sun during the day and during different seasons.

This is a very interesting project for students, but the teacher will have to do some scouting to find a wall with the proper exposure. On a particular day of the week, each week of the school year, the students will go out to the playground and place the staff in a marked location. You will need to use the level to be certain that the staff is perpendicular to the horizon. The shadow cast by the edge of the staff should be marked and dated on the wall.

As weeks progress, students will begin to see the change in position of the sun as days become shorter. This graphic evidence will stimulate numerous classroom conversations regarding daylight savings time, trajectory of the sun, solar heating, and time zones.

Students can mark the wall once each week at a specific time, but the two marks on a specific day show the actual movement of the sun across the sky.

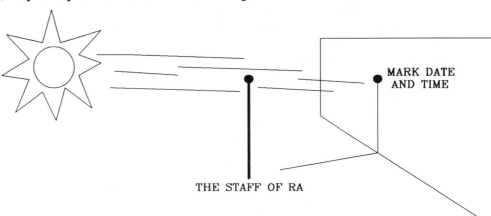

MARK DATE AND TIME

THE STAFF OF RA

Hands On, Inc
2121 Rebild Drive
Solvang, CA 93463

<table>
<tr><td>**4**</td><td>**Identifies AM/PM and Time Zone Relationships and Purposes**</td></tr>
</table>

Only the Shadow Knows!
Grade Level: Upper

MATERIALS: Plywood or clay sundial bases (heavy paper plates can also be used), protractors, tagboard, scissors, and masking tape.

ORGANIZATION: Teams of two or three students

PROCEDURE: Two aspects of this lesson fit into the concepts of measurement. First, use of the protractor to mark the latitude angle; and second, a concrete example of the movement of the sun and the need for time zones.

Some basic information which students will need is the latitude of the school. You can find this information in an almanac or atlas (see Appendix H).

Begin by explaining that the sundial has been used for telling time since 2000 B.C. The sundial works because the earth revolves as it rotates around the sun thus causing the sun to look as though it is changing position in the sky. This change of position follows the same arc everyday at the same time.

Have students take plywood, a clay slab, or a paper plate and mark it similarly to the sample below. Next, have them cut a right triangle of cardboard or plywood by measuring an angle to match your school's latitude. Tape the gnomon (the arm of the sundial) to the dial face so it points to 12 o'clock.

Take the sundials outside and point the gnomon to due north. The shadow created by the sun should point to the correct time. If there are discrepancies check that the angle is correct, that the gnomon points due north, or that you have accounted for daylight savings time.

Extension topics include a project to mount a permanent school sundial, a research study on Stonehenge, or a project in which students research and make other types of calendars.

Hands On, Inc
2121 Rebild Drive
Solvang, CA 93463

5	**Uses a Stop Watch and Can Read Time to the 10th of a Second**

A Time for Estimates

Grade Level: Upper

MATERIALS: Stop watches or digital watches with stop watch features, tally sheets (see below)

ORGANIZATION:

Teams of two, three, or four students

PROCEDURE:

In this activity, students will be estimating the number of seconds they think it will take to perform specific tasks. They will record their estimates and then perform the activities to see how accurate they were.

Give each student a tally sheet and time to discuss the various activities within their groups. Some possible activities include:
1. Counting to one hundred
2. Running back and forth across a court of some kind
3. A lap around a track
4. How long they stay in the air when jumping

Once students have made their estimates, let them test themselves to check for accuracy and record actual results in the third column of the tally sheet.

As a side activity, you might want to have students count "seconds" and see how close they can come to estimating the length of a minute. This activity is helpful to students in providing a frame of reference for future time estimation.

MAKE YOUR BEST GUESS

ACTIVITY	ESTIMATE	ACTUAL
COUNTING		
RUNNING		
ONE LAP		
IN THE AIR		

Hands On, Inc
2121 Rebild Drive
Solvang, CA 93463

5	**Uses a Stop Watch and Can Read Time to the 10th of a Second**

Drop Drill

Grade Level: Upper

MATERIALS: Stop watches or digital watches which have stop watch capability, various objects to drop, tape measure

ORGANIZATION: Teams of two, three, or four students

PROCEDURE: This activity allows students to estimate and then prove theories about the effect of gravity upon objects. They will drop objects from various heights and then time the tenths of seconds taken for these objects to hit the ground.

Begin by letting students drop an item from a height of one foot. Clicking the stop watch fast enough will be a problem so they will need to make the drop several times. They should record their "average" time.

Next, have students move to a two foot level and do the same, then to three, four and so on. See if students begin to see a pattern in the drop time from each level.

You might extend the lesson to have each group drop three or four different items and see if the weight of the object affects the time (it won't). A different approach would be to have each team drop a different item and then compare the times on a class chart.

HEIGHT	FIRST	SECOND	THIRD	AVERAGE
1 FT				
2 FT				
3 FT				
4 FT				
5 FT				

Hands On, Inc
2121 Rebild Drive
Solvang, CA 93463

5	**Uses a Stop Watch and Can Read Time to the 10th of a Second**

Lub Dub Goes My Heart
Grade Level: Upper

MATERIALS: Stop watches or digital watches with stop watch features, tally sheets.

ORGANIZATION: Teams of three or four students

PROCEDURE: In this lesson, students will combine a study of aerobic exercises with use of the stopwatch for recording pulse rate.

Begin by discussing the heart and its function — to pump blood through the body. Ask students to identify times when their pulse rate seems to be faster. This should include time of physical exertion and stress.

Discuss the concept of aerobics and that it focuses on identifying the pulse rate of the body at rest and the pulse rate of the body after physical exercise. The third factor is the time it takes your pulse to return to its normal rate.

Using the stopwatch, have each group member take his/her pulse for one minute (you might have them do this for 30 seconds and multiply the pulse by two). Record the results.

STUDENT	Heartbeat at Rest	Heartbeat After Exercise	Return to Normal
Sarah			
Elaine			
Albert			
Eunice			

Have students then do some physical activity such as running and once again take the pulse rate, recording the results. At three minute intervals, continue to have students take their pulse and see how long it takes for the rate to return to normal.

As an extension, you might have children graph their pulse rates. This is especially effective for a double bar graph.

Hands On, Inc
2121 Rebild Drive
Solvang, CA 93463

5	**Uses a Stop Watch and Can Read Time to the 10th of a Second**

In the Blink of an Eye
Grade Level: Upper

MATERIALS: Magazines featuring photography (National Geographic, Life), scissors, construction or butcher paper.

ORGANIZATION: A whole class activity

PROCEDURE: This is an extension of the stopwatch concept introducing hundredths of seconds.

Have students go through a variety of magazines cutting out pictures of occurences which take short periods of time. Items might include fluttering hummingbird wings, blink of an eye, or snap of the fingers. Allow students time to be creative about their choices.

Once students have made selections, have the class work together to do research to find the time span involved in each of the pictured activities. You should assign a time frame to each picture — 1/100th of a second, 1/1000th of a second, etc.

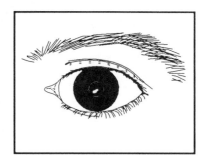

Next, have students create a "time" line placing these items in order from shortest time span to longest. Discuss the chart and relate it to time frames which students can more readily understand such as those mentioned in the previous stop watch lessons.

Hands On, Inc
2121 Rebild Drive
Solvang, CA 93463

| 6 | **Counts to a Monetary Value Using Coins of Mixed Value** |

Pass the Buck
Grade Level: Middle

MATERIALS: An assortment of coins for each child

ORGANIZATION: Groups of four

PROCEDURE: This is an activity in which children pass money around the table based on amounts called out by the teacher. The object of the game is for each student to end up with all of one type of coin. For example player 1 might collect all pennies, player 2 all nickels, etc. It will not be possible for this complete distribution to be attained, but it creates a strategy problem which the group must work together to solve.

Begin by giving each student a coin bank of equal amounts of pennies, nickels, dimes (and quarters if applicable to the grade level). Each group should determine the direction they will be passing coins and the denomination which each student will collect. Once this is accomplished, the teacher begins by reading (saying) a monetary amount -- "$.27." At this point each student passes 27 cents to the next person, counting it out as he does so. The trick is that the students collecting quarters should not pass any quarters (if they can help it); the dime students should pass no dimes (if they can help it), etc. Players must pass the right amount of money each turn. If they do not have the right amount of pennies, for example, the players collecting pennies must make change for them.

The first few rounds of this game will take some time for students to understand due to the nuances of the game, but once they understand the concept it provides excellent practice in making change.

Hands On, Inc
2121 Rebild Drive
Solvang, CA 93463

6	**Counts to a Monetary Value Using Coins of Mixed Value**

Spin to Win!
Grade Level: Middle

MATERIALS: Spinners divided into four to six sections (as below), an assortment of imitation coins (equal amount) for each student.

ORGANIZATION: Teams of two students

PROCEDURE: This is a game activity in which each student will be spinning a spinner and the student with the lowest amount of money on the spinner gives that amount of money to the other team member.

Have students make spinners (see Appendix A) and divide the surface into four to six areas. Have students randomly select a different amount to write in each section. Depending upon the sophistication of the students, you may want to set limits on the largest amount students should write. You might also make stipulations such as each number written must be at least five cents larger than the previous number. This will allow for a variety of winners.

Give each student an assortment of coins—at least three times as much as the highest number on the spinner.

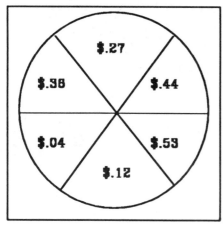

Begin the game by having both players spin their spinners. The student who spins the <u>smaller</u> number should give that amount to the other team member. Players continue this process of the lower number paying the player with the larger number.

The winner of the game is the student who wins all of the other student's coins. To change the numbers, have students rotate spinners around the room.

As an extension to this game, have <u>both</u> students give away the amount of money they spin. In this case, the player who spins the higher numbers will give his coins away first.

Hands On, Inc
2121 Rebild Drive
Solvang, CA 93463

6	**Counts to a Monetary Value Using Coins of Mixed Value**

You Can Bank on It
Grade Level: Middle

MATERIALS: Imitation coins for each student (see Appendix B), small paper bags

ORGANIZATION: Teams of two, three, or four students

PROCEDURE: Tell students that they are going to imagine that they have just opened their piggy banks and have a large number of pennies, nickels, and dimes (quarters as well, if age appropriate). Using these coins they will discover different ways to make various sums of money.

Hand out a bag of coins (piggy bank) to each group and have them empty the coins onto their desks. Begin with simple quantities such as five, ten, and fifteen cents. Have teams work together to discover the various combinations of coins which are possible to total these amounts.

Once students get the idea of the lesson, let each team member have an opportunity to ask another team member to combine various amounts. Students should check one another's responses.

6	**Counts to a Monetary Value Using Coins of Mixed Value**

Lose, and WIN!
Grade Level: Middle

MATERIALS: An assortment of coins for each student, a pair of dice (or one octagon die)

ORGANIZATION: Teams of three or four students

PROCEDURE: This is a game in which students practice counting to given monetary amounts by using a strategy which will allow them to "lose" all of their coins. The first player to place all of his coins in the center of the table is the winner.

Give each student a "bank" of money with each person receiving the same number of each coin type. For example, if you want your students to work with dimes and quarters in particular, give each student more of that coin type.

The game begins with player 1 rolling one or two dice (once again depending upon the level of the game) and as he rolls, the "coin call " is made -- eg. "nickels." Each student then looks at the dice numbers and has to figure the value of that number of nickels. If student 1 were to roll a 3, the value would be $.15. Each player then takes this amount of money and places it in front of his bank. If he is correct, his money goes to the center of the table, if he is incorrect, the money goes back into his bank. Group members check for correct answers. Player 2 then rolls and makes another coin call.

The strategy of the game calls for students to use various combinations of coins. The student who automatically chooses three nickels to make the 15 cent total (continues to use all of one coin type rather than varying denominations) will soon find that he does not have enough possible combinations to form the right amount of change and cannot get rid of the coins as fast as players who have used more varied combinations of coins.

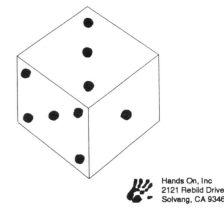

Hands On, Inc
2121 Rebild Drive
Solvang, CA 93463

7	**Makes Change Using Pennies, Nickels, Dimes, and Quarters**

Making a Change
Grade Level: Middle/Upper

MATERIALS: An assortment of coins for each student (see Appendix B)

ORGANIZATION: A whole class, half-class, or small group activity

PROCEDURE: This is a relay but not necessarily a race (unless the teacher wishes to add this element).

Begin by giving each student a bank of coins and explain that there are numerous combinations of coins to total a given amount. Generally, when people give change, they try to give as few coins as possible. In this relay, students are going to create as many different combinations of coins for a given amount as possible. Each class member will be responsible for creating a new combination when his turn arrives.

Number the students 1 through ? and draw a chart on the board similar to that shown. You may be the recorder, or you may choose a student to perform this task. Begin with the amount "37 cents" and let student 1 create a combination; record it on the chart. Let student 2 create a second combination and record it. Continue this procedure until all students have had an opportunity to respond. Encourage your students to be planning their combinations ahead of time.

	Pennies	Nickels	Dimes	Quarters	Total
Student 1					
Student 2					
Student 3					
Student 4					
Student 5					
Student 6					
Student 7					

Hands On, Inc
2121 Rebild Drive
Solvang, CA 93463

7	**Makes Change Using Pennies, Nickels, Dimes, and Quarters**

Out for a Spin

Grade Level: Middle/Upper

MATERIALS: Spinners as described in Appendix A, an assortment of coins for each group

ORGANIZATION: Teams of two students

PROCEDURE: Have each student make a spinner and divide the spinner surface into 6 sections (similar to that shown). On each section have students write in different monetary amounts (the teacher should determine the maximum amount depending upon class ability).

The procedures of the game are dependent upon the skill you are trying to teach (addition or subtraction). For an addition activity, have both students spin the spinners. Students should count out the amount of money shown by the spinner and place this amount in the center of the table. Student 1 should count the money while student 2 does the mental arithmetic of adding the two figures together in his head. In this way, students get the practice of physically counting money and also the instant feedback of knowing whether or not the mental arithmetic is correct. Students switch roles with each spin of the spinner.

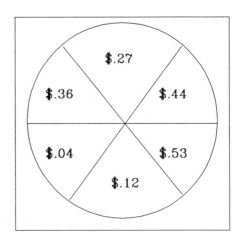

As a subtraction activity, have the student who spins the highest number make change for the difference between the two spins. Once students have worked with the numbers on their own spinners, rotate the spinners around the room so they continually work with new figures.

Hands On, Inc
2121 Rebild Drive
Solvang, CA 93463

7	## Makes Change Using Pennies, Nickels, Dimes, and Quarters

HANDO
Grade Level: Middle/Upper

MATERIALS:　　Hando cards (Appendix C), Hando markers

ORGANIZATION: Individually or in teams of two students.

PROCEDURE:　　This is a game which is a take-off of Bingo in which students have to figure correct amounts of change.

There are a variety of approaches you can use. We will explain a very simple form of the game and then point out some areas which can be embellished.

Begin by giving each student a Hando card. Have them mark each square with a number divisible by five (a nickel). Students may place a marker on the free space. Tell students to imagine that they have $1.00, and as the teacher calls out various numbers, the students must figure the amount of change they would receive. If they happen to have that amount on the Hando card, they get to mark that square. A record of the numbers called should be kept on the board.

H	A	N	D	O
		FREE SPACE		

For example, the teacher might call "25 cents." The change from $1.00 would be 75 cents. If a student has 75 cents written in one of the squares, a marker should be placed on the square. Continue with this procedure until a student wins the game (five markers in a row).

If students are capable of working with pennies in their change, you might have students work with amounts less than 25 cents, then less than 50 cents, etc. In these cases, the students should begin with a total amount of 25 cents or 50 cents respectively, rather than $1.00.

Hands On, Inc
2121 Rebild Drive
Solvang, CA 93463

7	**Makes Change Using Pennies, Nickels, Dimes, and Quarters**

That's an Order!

Grade Level: Middle/Upper

MATERIALS: Construction paper, pens, and an assortment of coins and dollar bills (see Appendix B) for each student

ORGANIZATION: Teams of two, three, or four students

PROCEDURE: This is a combination creative writing and math lesson in which children will be creating a menu and then make change for the various items on the menu.

Tell students that they are now restaurant owners and one of their first tasks is to create a menu which is interesting and has varied but fair prices. Each group should be responsible for creating one menu.

Once this is done, allow groups to order from one another's menus and then pay for their meals. You will need dollar bills as well as change for the students.

There are various skills which are practiced in this lesson including addition and subtraction of money and making change.

If students get especially involved with the lesson you can do a whole class project on design of menus and invite another class to come to your "restaurant" for lunch.

Chez Hand-out		Beverages	
Hamburger Specialties		Root Beer Float	1.25
Buffalo Burger	2.45	Orange Juice	.95
Oregon Burger	3.05	Cola	.50
Potato Burger	2.25	Orange Drink	.50
Plain Burger	1.95	Milk Shake	1.45
Side Orders		Chocolate, Vanilla	
French Fries	.95		
Cole Slaw	.65	**Desserts**	
Baked Potato	.80	Hot Fudge Sundae	1.30
Salad	1.20	Apple Pie	1.55

 Hands On, Inc
2121 Rebild Drive
Solvang, CA 93463

8	# Identifies Quarters, Half-Dollars, and Dollars and States Their Respective and Equivalent Values

Cut Your Bills

Grade Level: Middle

MATERIALS: Dollar samples (Appendix B), scissors, envelopes

ORGANIZATION: Individually or in teams of two students

PROCEDURE: Give each student or team a sample dollar (below), scissors, and an envelope.

Begin the lesson by asking students the value of one dollar. Write the various equivalencies to a dollar on the board as students generate ideas — four quarters, ten dimes, etc.

Now cut the sample dollar in half and discuss the value of one-half dollar. Finally, cut the bill into ten equal pieces and question students about the value. Depending upon the skill of students, you may also cut the dime pieces in half to form nickel pieces.

Take a second sample dollar and cut into random pieces. Hold up a few of the pieces and ask students to estimate the amount represented. They should list as many money combinations as possible.

As a final step in this activity, give a sample dollar and an envelope to each student. Have students cut various sized pieces and place them in an envelope. Exchange envelopes among groups and have students try to figure out different coin combinations to equal the "symbolic" money amounts.

Hands On, Inc
2121 Rebild Drive
Solvang, CA 93463

8	# Identifies Quarters, Half-Dollars, and Dollars and States Their Respective and Equivalent Values

Do It My Way
Grade Level: Middle

MATERIALS: An assortment of coins (Appendix B) for each student, equivalency cards (Appendix D)

ORGANIZATION: A whole class activity with a student leader

PROCEDURE: This lesson will give students practice in finding different coin combinations to make a given denomination.

Hand out a coin bank to each student; this should include several pennies, nickels, dimes, and quarters. As practice, call out an amount — $.72 cents. Ask students to assemble change to total this amount and then go around the room asking children to describe the number of each coin they used.

Tell students that the purpose of the game they will be playing is to try to match the same coin configuration as the person who calls the number. For example, if the total is $.72, the caller may have 2 quarters, 2 dimes, and 2 pennies. In order to become the next caller, your configuration must match the caller's.

Begin by selecting a student to come forward. Have him select an equivalency card and let him select a coin combination from a bank in the front of the room. Have him call out the amount. Give students time to choose a combination of coins. When they have done so have them raise their hands. The caller calls on classmates to respond. As soon as a student has the right combination of coins, he becomes the new caller.

Once the students know this game it can be extended to use dollars, half dollars and larger bills.

Hands On, Inc
2121 Rebild Drive
Solvang, CA 93463

8	**Identifies Quarters, Half-Dollars, and Dollars and States Their Respective and Equivalent Values**

Natural Money

Grade Level: Middle

MATERIALS: Containers for collecting various natural materials, egg cartons, muffin tins, or paper cups, and market advertisements

ORGANIZATION: Teams of three or four students.

PROCEDURE: In this activity, students will be collecting a variety of natural materials (pebbles, seed pods, shells, etc.). Begin by giving the homework assignment of collecting numerous natural artifacts. Some items might be returned in prolific numbers and some might be very rare. This supply and demand concept is the backbone of this lesson.

When students bring their found items to school, have each group divide items into egg cartons or muffin tins. From this information, have them create a monetary system within the group (i.e., four white pebbles equals one large smooth rock, five smooth rocks equal one acorn, etc.). Ask students to record these values on a chart for reference.

Once each group has established its system, give groups a supermarket advertisement and let them set prices. A variety of activities can be done at this point. Let students purchase various items from the market ad and make "change" for one another within the group; do a barter system of exchange between the various groups; or combine all of the various collections and create a classwide money system.

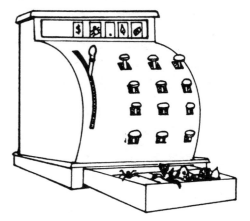

Hands On, Inc
2121 Rebild Drive
Solvang, CA 93463

8	# Identifies Quarters, Half-Dollars, and Dollars and States Their Respective and Equivalent Values

Balance of Power
Grade Level: Middle

MATERIALS: Rope for a tug of war, labels for pinning on shirts

ORGANIZATION: A whole class activity

PROCEDURE: In this activity, students will conduct a whole class tug of war with the hope of completely equalizing the tugging teams.

Make up a set of name tags which say "quarter," "half dollar," and "dollar." Walk around the room randomly giving each class member a tag. Tell them that their challenge will be to do a tug of war but they have to divide themselves into teams of equal monetary value. The name tag they received tells their value.

Select one student as the organizer — this student will not participate in the tugs, but will direct students back and forth to equalize pulling power. To encourage students to achieve the "balance of power" think of some type of class prize (no homework for a night) to encourage the cooperative aspects of this activity.

To help explain the format, imagine a class of 21 students - 7 dollar, 7 half-dollar and 7 quarter students. The first organization is shown below (note that the teams must be of equal monetary value or at least as close as possible — in this case within $.25.

TEAM A	**TEAM B**
$1.00 $1.00 $1.00 $.50 $.50 $.50 $.50 $.25 $.25 $.25 $.25 $.25	$1.00 $1.00 $1.00 $1.00 $.50 $.50 $.50 $.25 $.25

Imagine that team A wins. You must strengthen team B and you do this by making change. Perhaps exchanging a $1.00 player for 2 quarters and 1 half-dollar. The new teams look like this:

TEAM A	**TEAM B**
$1.00 $1.00 $1.00 $1.00 $.50 $.50 $.50 $.25 $.25 $.25	$1.00 $1.00 $1.00 $.50 $.50 $.50 $.50 $.25 $.25 $.25 $.25

Continue with this process until teams balance monetarily as well as physically.

Hands On, Inc
2121 Rebild Drive
Solvang, CA 93463

9	**Identifies and Writes Value for a Given Amount Using Dollar Sign and Decimal Place**

Orderly Money
Grade Level: Middle

MATERIALS: Dice, paper and pencil

ORGANIZATION: Individually or in teams of two students

PROCEDURE: This is a very basic activity in writing specific monetary amounts.

Give each group or student TWO PAIR (four) dice and let them roll. Imagine that the numbers rolled are 6-3-5-1. Have students place the numbers from largest to smallest 6-5-3-1 and then write this amount on their papers $65.31. Next, have them reverse the dice so they are ordered from smallest to largest 1-3-5-6 and have them write this number $13.56.

Each time students write a number, they should read the dollar amount to their partners.

Have students repeat this procedure several times using two, three, or four dice. Reinforce the use of the dollar sign and the decimal point.

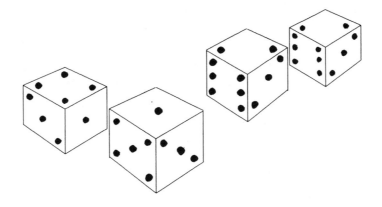

 Hands On, Inc
2121 Rebild Drive
Solvang, CA 93463

9	**Identifies and Writes Value for a Given Amount Using Dollar Sign and Decimal Place**

Read and Write Right
Grade Level: Middle

MATERIALS: A teacher prepared list of monetary values appropriate to grade level

ORGANIZATION: A whole class activity

PROCEDURE: This lesson provides experience for children to write figures on the chalkboard after reading them from an overhead.

Begin the lesson by dividing the class into four or five teams. One team member from each team should go to the chalkboard prepared to write a monetary amount. The teacher then shows an overhead transparency saying, "Twenty-five dollars and thirty-five cents." Each team member attempts to write this amount on the board ($25.35).

To eliminate competition or embarrassment by students who have difficulty with this, a team member may elect to have a group conference to check the answer. That team member is the one who must do the writing. If the response is correct (including dollar sign and decimal point) the team receives a point.

Have a second team member come to the board for the next monetary amount and continue the process. The interaction within the groups and the transfer of written numbers to digits is the focus of this lesson.

Hands On, Inc
2121 Rebild Drive
Solvang, CA 93463

9	**Identifies and Writes Value for a Given Amount Using Dollar Sign and Decimal Place**

Wildcard
Grade Level: Middle

MATERIALS: Construction paper, markers

ORGANIZATION: A whole class activity

PROCEDURE: Students often have a difficult time writing monetary amounts which have zeroes. This exercise provides practice in reading and figuring these types of numbers.

Prepare a group of cards (12" by 24" construction paper) similar to those shown below. Include the dollar sign and decimal point. Hand these cards out to various students and then call out numbers for them to display at the front of the room.

For example, say, "one dollar and forty-one cents." With this instruction, the dollar sign, the decimal point, the "1", a second "1" and the "4" should go to the front of the room and place themselves in proper order to show $.1.41. Continue this process and every now and then say "WILDCARD." The wildcard is a zero that can go forward at any time and change the value of the display. As soon as the Wildcard is in place, the entire class should read the amount displayed.

This physical participation will keep all students interested and involved in the activity. As time progresses you may wish to have more than one wildcard.

As an extension, ask students displaying numbers to rearrange themselves to form the largest and smallest possible dollar amounts.

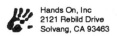
Hands On, Inc
2121 Rebild Drive
Solvang, CA 93463

<table>
<tr><td>**9**</td><td>## Identifies and Writes Value for a Given Amount Using Dollar Sign and Decimal Place</td></tr>
</table>

Funny Money
Grade Level: Middle

MATERIALS: Various geometric shapes (circles, squares, rectangles) for each student, scissors

ORGANIZATION: Teams of two, three, or four students

PROCEDURE: This lesson is an abstract version of money cutting as described in a previous lesson. In this case, the geometric shape will symbolize a particular dollar value.

Give each team of students a set of shapes. The shapes should be distributed so that one student on each team has all circles, one student has all squares, etc. The reason for using different shapes is that students will have to continue to think abstractly rather than focus on one type of shape. One team member should call out a random monetary amount (i.e. $1.55). Other team members should then begin planning a set of cutouts which abstractly depicts this amount. The figure shown below depicts the $1.55 and is cut from a square shape.

Continue this process until each team member has had two or three opportunities to call out an amount.

As an extension you may wish to have students paste their cut outs on construction paper, label the amounts, and post them on the wall. Discuss each amount and have students discuss alternative methods of depicting this amount.

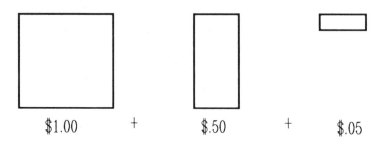

$1.00   + $.50   + $.05

 Hands On, Inc
2121 Rebild Drive
Solvang, CA 93463

10	**Adds and Subtracts (Makes Change for) Money Value up to Four Digits**

Mail Order Mania
Grade Level: Middle

MATERIALS: Mail order catalogs for each group of students, calculators are optional.

ORGANIZATION: Teams of two, three, or four students

PROCEDURE: This is a basic activity in addition and subtraction of money.

Begin by having students select a catalog of interest to them. Tell the class that they are going to prepare a mail order form for purchasing several catalog items. They will have to figure sales tax and shipping cost as well.

Have students make purchases and complete an order form. You may want to create a minimum order amount or perhaps tell students that they are to spend as close to $100.00 as possible.

One extension involves having students order a complete wardrobe, furnishings for a house, tools for a shop, or kitchen utensils and appliances. This can all be tied in to a unit on occupations and planning for the future.

HANDS ON, INC.

Mail Order Department

Number	Item	Unit Price	Total
1	Wonderful Toy	12.95	12.95
1	Magical Toy	3.95	3.95
2	Extraordinary Toy	15.95	31.90
	Subtotal		48.80
	Tax		2.93
	Handling		2.00
	TOTAL		53.73

Hands On, Inc
2121 Rebild Drive
Solvang, CA 93463

10	**Adds and Subtracts (Makes Change for) Money Value up to Four Digits**

Mmm.. Good!

Grade Level: Middle/Upper

MATERIALS: A small package of M and M's for each group

ORGANIZATION: Teams of two, three, or four students

PROCEDURE: This is a lesson in estimation and addition and multiplication of "monetary" amounts.

Have students feel the bag of M and M's and estimate the number of candies in the bag without opening it. Ask students if they remember the colors in an M and M bag (light brown, dark brown, green, red, yellow, orange) and tell them that each color has a certain value but do not tell this value.

$.50 each $.25 each $.15 each $.10 each $.05 each $.01 each

Based upon the figures have them estimate the value of the contents of their unopened bag. They should write their estimates down and should talk about how these estimates were determined. Have each group share the "what and why" of their estimates. Open the bags and allow students to count the number of candies and let them re-estimate their guesses (they still know only the values, not the color for each value).

Finally, assign the value for each color as follows:

The color which has the fewest color M and M's is worth $.50
The color which has the next fewest color of M and M's in worth $.25
The color which has the next fewest color of M and M's is worth $.15
The color which has the next fewest color of M and M's is worth $.10
The color which has the nest fewest is worth $.05
The most prominent color is worth $.01

Let students figure the value and then reverse the order.

As a final activity, let students eat their "money."

Hands On, Inc
2121 Rebild Drive
Solvang, CA 93463

10	**Adds and Subtracts (Makes Change for) Money Value up to Four Digits**

Turnabout is Fair Play
Grade Level: Middle/Upper

MATERIALS: An assortment of coins for each student, dice

ORGANIZATION: Teams of two or four students

PROCEDURE: This lesson is similar to "Orderly Money" in that students will be using the dice to determine specific monetary amounts.

In this activity, student 1 will roll the dice and then place them in numerical order from largest to smallest 6-4-2-1. This amount is equivalent to $64.21. Student 2 should take this amount from the "bank" and place it in the center of the table. Both students should write this number down on a piece of scratch paper.

Student 2 then rolls the dice and places the numbers in order from smallest to largest 1-3-3-6 (equivalent to $13.36). Student 1 then removes this amount from the stack of money in the center of the table.

Both students then compute (subtract) roll 2 from roll 1 on scratch paper and tell the amount of "change" which is left. The students count the money to see if their answers are correct.

Extensions to this activity are numerous but a simple idea is to have Student 1 roll dice and have both students compute the high to low amount, the low to high amount, and then make change without using any paper and pencil. You may want to begin this process by using two dice, eventually adding a third and fourth.

Hands On, Inc
2121 Rebild Drive
Solvang, CA 93463

10	**Adds and Subtracts (Makes Change for) Money Value up to Four Digits**

Make It or Break It
Grade Level: Middle/Upper

MATERIALS: Equivalency cards (see Appendix D), money cutouts (Appendix A)

ORGANIZATION: Divide students into teams of two

PROCEDURE: Depending upon the grade level and the skill of students, this lesson can be done for a variety of monetary amounts. The directions remain the same regardless of the amounts you choose to use.

Each team should place a stack of equivalency cards between them and take a specified (by the teacher) amount of money from the bank. Player 1 begins by selecting a card. Player 2 must then count out that amount of money and give it to player 1. Player 2 then draws and player 1 counts out that amount of money and gives it to player 2.

The game continues in this manner until one of the players has an insufficient amount to make the "payment."

Equivalency cards are organized as follows:
        Cards 1-9 amounts achieved by using dimes -- 10, 20, 30 cents
        Cards 10-19 amounts achieved by using nickels and dimes -- 5, 15, 25 cents
        Cards 20-27 miscellaneous amounts

A blank page of equivalency cards has been provided in Appendix D so that you can make your own cards.

[8] 80 CENTS $.80	[17] 70 CENTS $.70	[26] 35 CENTS $.35

Hands On, Inc
2121 Rebild Drive
Solvang, CA 93463

11	**Multiplies and Divides Monetary Amounts by Whole Numbers**

Hoagies, Subs, and Torpedoes
Grade Level: Upper

MATERIALS: Paper towel or gift wrapping rolls for each team, rulers, scissors

ORGANIZATION: Teams of two, three, or four students

PROCEDURE: In this lesson, students will be dividing an imaginary submarine sandwich (paper towel roll) into monetary sections. Begin by explaining that students are going to a deli to lunch with some of their friends and have decided to order a 15 inch-long submarine sandwich. Each student has different amounts of money; therefore, each student will receive a different amount of sandwich. Students will need to cut the sandwich into the correct lengths.

We have provided three different scenarios: easy, moderate, and challenging.

Easy sandwich costs $15.00		Middle sandwich costs $15.00		Challenging sandwich costs $15.00	
Bill	$3.00	Bill	$3.50	Bill	$3.75
Tony	$3.00	Tony	$3.50	Tony	$2.75
Rhonda	$2.00	Rhonda	$ .50	Rhonda	$ .75
Albert	$1.00	Albert	$2.50	Albert	$2.50
Ben	$4.00	Ben	$2.00	Ben	$4.50
Allie	$2.00	Allie	$3.00	Allie	$ .75

11	**Multiplies and Divides Monetary Amounts by Whole Numbers**

Candy Equivalents
Grade Level: Upper

MATERIALS: Assorted boxed candy (Juju Bees, Skittles, etc.)

ORGANIZATION: Teams of two students

PROCEDURE: Provide a box of candy for each team of students and tell them they will have to create a monetary system for the colors of candy. The rule which makes this activity difficult is that each candy must be worth a "whole cent" amount (no fractional pennies).

The larger variety of candy colors in the box, the more difficult the problem becomes. For example:

Candy color	Number of candies	Value of candy	Total value
Red	8	.09 each	$.72
Green	3	.03 each	$.09
Yellow	9	.72 each	$6.48

The monetary system created is:

        3 greens = 1 red
        24 greens = 1 yellow
        8 reds   = 1 yellow

If students cannot create a system using all of the candies of each color, have them develop the best system they can using as many candies as possible. Have them look through catalogs for items to purchase and then figure out the price in candy money. For example, if an item were $8.95 in a catalog, the student would need to pay with 12 yellows, 2 reds, and 2 greens. As an added incentive within the group. Let the student who comes up with the right answer first, eat one piece of his "money."

Hands On, Inc
2121 Rebild Drive
Solvang, CA 93463

11	# Multiplies and Divides Monetary Amounts by Whole Numbers

Divide and Conquer
Grade Level: Upper

MATERIALS: 3" to 5" circles cut from construction paper, scissors

ORGANIZATION: Teams of two or three students

PROCEDURE: In this lesson, students will be dividing money into various parts. To create a more concrete experience, you may wish to use the sample dollars as described in the lesson, "Cut Your Bills" (Task Analysis 14). We suggest you use circles to help students understand the more abstract approach to division of money.

Give each group of students 20 circles and tell them that each circle represents one dollar. Using five of the circles, ask students to divide them equally into five groups (one circle per group). Next, ask students how they would divide the five circles in 10 equal parts (cut them in half). Finally, ask students how they would divide the circles into 2 equal parts (cut one circle in half so each part would receive two and one-half circles).

The puzzle which each group is going to ponder is how to cut the circles so they can be divided equally into three and four groups. Give each team time to discuss and create a solution to these problems.

When students have finished this task, ask them to take a third set of five circles and divide them into 6, 7, 8, or 9 parts and glue their responses on to a large sheet of construction paper.

Each group should then post their "division creation" and classmates should work together to decide the amount represented by the various pieces in each group..

$5.00 Divided into four groups $5.00 Divided into three groups

| 11 | **Multiplies and Divides Monetary Amounts by Whole Numbers** |

Division is Sweet
Grade Level: Upper

MATERIALS: A different roll of assorted candy for each student in each group (Life Savers, Smartees, Necco Wafers, etc.)

ORGANIZATION: Groups of four students

PROCEDURE: In this lesson students will be dividing money indirectly. Begin by giving each group member a different roll of assorted candy. Each group should have the same assortment. On the board write the cost of each roll and have students compute a per piece price for each candy. For example, if a roll of Life Savers cost 25 cents and if there are 9 Life Savers per package, one Life Saver would cost 2.8 cents (.25 ÷ 9 = 2.8 cents (you might choose to use even numbers to start out with). Do this computation for each assorted roll.

The next challenge is for students to divide the four candy types into a portion for each student so that 1) each student has the same candy value; and, 2) so that no student has the same number of any type of candy.

For example: Life Savers = 2.8 cents each
                 Smartees = 1 cent each
                 Necco Wafers = .5 cents each
                 Gobstoppers = 2 cents each

Student 1		Student 2		Student 3		Student 4	
2 Life Savers	3 cents	3 Life Savers	6 cents	4 Life Savers	12 cents	0 Life Savers	0 cents
6 Gobstoppers	12 cents	4 Gobstoppers	8 cents	0 Gobstoppers	0 cents	5 Gobstoppers	10 cents
10 Necco Wafers	5 cents	2 Necco Wafers	1 cents	8 Necco Wafers	4 cents	14 Necco Wafers	7 cents
0 Smartees	0 cents	5 Smartees	5 cents	4 Smartees	4 cents	3 Smartees	3 cents

All students' candy totals 20 cents

Hands On, Inc
2121 Rebild Drive
Solvang, CA 93463

12	**Compares, Estimates, and Measures Length (height) in Inches, Feet, Yards, and in Metric Measures**

Relative to What?

Grade Level: Middle

MATERIALS: Strips of paper of various lengths, a list of 15 to 20 standard classroom items, pencils, tally sheets as shown

ORGANIZATION: Groups of two, three, or four students

PROCEDURE: Tell students that they are going to create a measurement table. Each table will list various items in the classroom and the length (width) of each item.

Each team should be given a strip of paper for measuring, but all of these strips should be of different lengths (units). Have students circulate the room measuring the listed items and marking down the linear measurement on their tally sheets.

Once this information has been compiled, ask each team to transfer its information to a chart on the wall. Discuss the reasons for the discrepancies in the linear measurements.

Ask students to come up with solutions to the discrepancy problem. Their responses will include reference to inches, feet, and yards, but you should include metric measurements as well. Discuss the need for standardization of measurement and the fact that many different cultures have their own standard (i.e., Standard vs. Metric).

Extensions include studies of ancient civilization measurement devices, a list of the benefits of standard measures, or a class project in which students create their own measurement system.

Item Measured	Units
Width of door	8
Length of flag	7
Height of teacher's chair	5
Length of reading table	9
Height of light switch	8
One floor tile	4
Mr. Smith's thumbnail	1/10
Width of the room	33
Thickness of math book	1/8
Height of chalk tray	5

Hands On, Inc
2121 Rebild Drive
Solvang, CA 93463

12	Compares, Estimates, and Measures Length (height) in Inches, Feet, Yards, and in Metric Measures

A New "Hand Book"
Grade Level: Middle

MATERIALS: Rulers for each student, a tally sheet for recording measurement results

ORGANIZATION: Teams of two or three students

PROCEDURE: Students will be creating a "hands" measurement page in which they measure classmates and objects around the room using their hands and then translate hand measurements into inches and feet and metric units.

Begin by explaining that horses are measured by hands and ask if this measurement would be accurate or not. To test the accuracy of this measurement method, students will be measuring one another as well as other classroom objects by hands. The teacher might need to demonstrate and stress that fingers should be closed tightly and hands placed closely together.

On the tally sheet, have each student write the names of five students and five other classroom objects to measure. To measure students, have them stand with their backs to the chalkboard and mark their heights with chalk (write names above chalk marks). Students should record their results on their tally sheets.

Upon completion of hand measuring, have students measure their hands with a ruler and convert the various hand measures into inches. To complete the lesson, select a few students for comparison purposes and record the hand measurements of several students. Discuss the accuracy of the results.

Student Names	# of Hands	Objects	# of Hands

Hands On, Inc
2121 Rebild Drive
Solvang, CA 93463

12	Compares, Estimates, and Measures Length (height) in Inches, Feet, Yards, and in Metric Measures

Motocross

Grade Level: Middle

MATERIALS: Motocross racetrack (Appendix G), ruler or measuring device, pencil, one die or spinner for each student.

ORGANIZATION: Teams of two students

PROCEDURE: This activity is appropriate for a variety of age levels by making the amount of distance to be measured a variable. Third grade students may measure to the 1/2 inch. Eighth grade students might measure to the 1/16th inch.

Both players begin at the START line with a pencil dot. Player 1 rolls the die and makes a line of that length (if players are using 1/4 inch measures and roll a 5, they should draw a line 5/4 or 1 and 1/4 inches long). Player 2 then rolls and makes a pencil line of the appropriate length. The procedure continues until one of the players crosses the finish line. This lesson can also be used with millimeters and centimeters if your students are working in the metric system.

Rather than use two dice for small increments (1/8 and 1/16 inch), each die spot might represent 2, 3, or 4 units of that length (a roll of "3" would be equal to 3/16 or 3/8). This will speed up the play of the game.

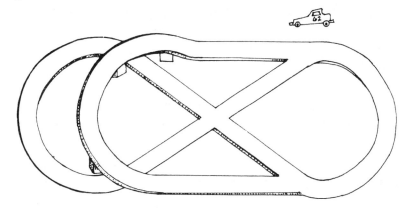

12	**Compares, Estimates, and Measures Length (height) in Inches, Feet, Yards, and in Metric Measures**

A Walking Ruler

Grade Level: Middle

MATERIALS: Rulers and a tally sheet for each student

ORGANIZATION: To be done individually or in teams of two students

PROCEDURE: In this activity, students will be estimating the length of various body parts. The goal is to provide students with some tangible personal measurements on their bodies which will help them with estimating distances in the future.

Ask all students to show you the length of an inch between their thumb and forefinger, a foot and a yard (a centimeter and meter) between their two hands. Tell students that they will be be estimating the length of various parts of their bodies and then measuring to see how accurate they were in their guesses.

Have students generate a list including such things as elbow to tip of finger, between the eyes, length of nose, height with arms extended, etc.

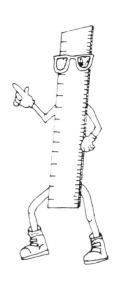

As a second step, allow students to use rulers to measure actual sizes of these same features and write the actual measurements in the second column. Ask students to circle that body part most closely measuring one inch, one foot, and one yard. In addition you might want students to pay particular attention to their overall height as this is a very meaningful way of estimating length.

As a final step, allow students time to circulate the room measuring various objects with their "model" body measurements. Let them see that even though these measurements may not be exact, they are very, very close to the true measurement. Reinforce this lesson often until students have a feel for this type of estimation.

Hands On, Inc
2121 Rebild Drive
Solvang, CA 93463

13	**Measures and Computes Perimeter in Standard and in Metric Units**

The Last Straw

Grade Level: Middle/Upper

MATERIALS: Straws, string, scissors, and rulers for each child

ORGANIZATION: Individually or in teams of two students

PROCEDURE: Have students measure their straws and cut them at 6" lengths. Using four 6" pieces, have them thread string through all four straws and then tie the string end to tend (thus creating a square).

As students look at the square, ask them for words which describe the straw sides — words such as "edges," "rim," "outside," etc. will be used. Eventually, elicit and define the word PERIMETER.

Since each straw is 6" long, ask students to compute the perimater of the square. Next, ask students to bed the straws to create different shapes, each time asking for a response of the perimeter length. Each shape will obviously have the same perimeter, but allow students to measure to find this out for themselves.

Hands On, Inc
2121 Rebild Drive
Solvang, CA 93463

| **13** | **Measures and Computes Perimeter in Standard and in Metric Units** |

String Rings

Grade Level: Middle/Upper

MATERIALS: String, scissors, paper and pencil

ORGANIZATION: Groups of two, three, or four students

PROCEDURE: Tell students that they are going to do some estimating and measuring of perimeter. Each student should select five items in the classroom to measure. They may need some guidance as to appropriate two dimensional planes.

Have each group of students estimate the perimeter of five selected items by cutting a piece of string that they feel will wrap around the exterior. Have students tape these estimates to a piece of construction paper labeling the items measured. Once these five estimates have been cut, have each group actually measure their five items with a new piece of string and cut an "actual size" piece for each item.

As a group, have students compare their estimates to the actual measurement.

As an extension, you might wish to have students measure the objects and then cut string to that length rather than measuring with string. This activity will move students to the more abstract concept of perimeter measurement.

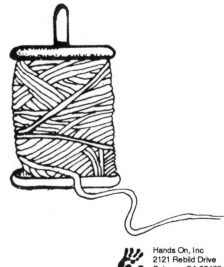

Hands On, Inc
2121 Rebild Drive
Solvang, CA 93463

13	**Measures and Computes Perimeter in Standard and in Metric Units**

Does Your School Measure Up?
Grade Level: Middle/Upper

MATERIALS: Toothpicks, sugar cubes, unifix cubes, or any other standard unit that can be lined up; a meter or yardstick (tape measure), a large board (plywood)

ORGANIZATION: Groups of four or as a whole class project

PROCEDURE: Students are going to create a scale model of the perimeter of their school in this activity. Depending upon the grade level, the class might do one or two of the buildings or the entire complex.

Armed with meter, yardsticks or other measuring devices, students should measure the various wall lengths at the school. As a group they will need to decide how to "scale" their model. One toothpick or sugar cube might equal one meter or 3 feet, for example.

Allow students to experiment with their model. They may wish to put in only exterior walls, but some will want to include all exterior walls and all room features as well. The purpose of this lesson is to provide practical measuring experiences. The "scaling" of a model is a sophisticated step in being able to convert inches to feet to yards or centimeters to meters.

As an extension, you may wish to have students do a similar project measuring a city block around the school. Another possibility is to include this lesson into a unit on map reading skills.

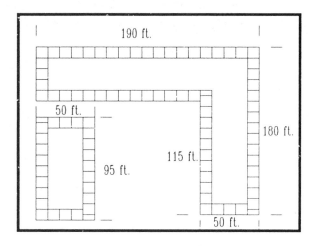

13	**Measures and Computes Perimeter in Standard and in Metric Units**

Equalizing Estimates
Grade Level: Middle/Upper

MATERIALS: Cardboard or construction paper (12" by 24"), scissors

ORGANIZATION: To be done individually

PROCEDURE: Students will be cutting out figures of various lengths and widths to help instill a concept of extimating inches and feet. The class will need to follow along with your instructions.

Begin by having students cut strips of construction paper to an estimated length — 1 inch, 3 inches, 6 inches, 1 foot, etc. (You can substitute metric measurements as well.) Each time they cut a strip, let them measure on a ruler and see how close they were to the actual distance. Some students will want to measure before they cut. Reinforce the idea that this is just practice and they should have fun guessing before they measure.

Once students understand the concept, begin asking them to cut specific shapes of specific sizes. For example, "cut out a rectangle that is 4 inches wide and 2 inches tall," or "cut out a circle that is 6 inches in diameter." After each cutting, let students measure results for accuracy. Once again, the important issue is not precision, it is the process and practice of estimation.

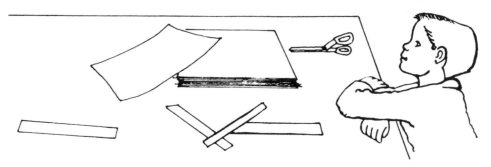

Hands On, Inc
2121 Rebild Drive
Solvang, CA 93463

14	**Converts Standard Measures of Inches, Feet, and Yards into Equivalent Values**

Measuring Up

Grade Level: Middle/Upper

MATERIALS: String, butcher paper, and measuring tapes

ORGANIZATION: Individually or in teams of two students

PROCEDURE: In this activity, students will measure the perimeter of their hands, feet, and bodies and will convert these measurements into inches, feet, and yards.

Give each student or team a long length of string (30 ft.) and tell them that they are to measure the distance around the contour of their hands (including fingers). Have them cut the string at the proper place and measure the length. Have them convert this to feet and to the fractional part of a yard. Students can use several methods to make this measurement so let them experiment with various methods.

Next, have each student estimate the distance around a shoe. Measure and complete the conversions. As a final activity, let students go outside onto the playground and draw an outline of their bodies with chalk or lay butcher paper on the floor and draw an outline of their body on it.. Measure this amount with string and then convert.

Given all of these pieces of string, have students compute the overall number of inches, feet, and yards in the outlines of the whole class. Ask them to figure how many classes it would take to measure a mile.

Hands On, Inc
2121 Rebild Drive
Solvang, CA 93463

14	**Converts Standard Measures of Inches, Feet, and Yards into Equivalent Values**

The Linear Olympics
Grade Level: Middle/Upper

MATERIALS: Tape measure, rulers, yardstick, softball

ORGANIZATION: To be done individually or as a whole class

PROCEDURE: You might wish to do this activity during PE time.

Begin by discussing the Olympics -- what they are and what they are for. Eventually move the discussion to the concept that the only way we know who wins any event is by some type of measurement. These measurements might be in <u>time</u> or in <u>distance</u>. In this activity we will be using the measurement of distance -- linear measurement.

Discuss each of the four events listed below but don't allow students to practice. On a tally sheet similar to that shown, have students estimate how well they think they will perform each event.

Give students time to fill out their estimates.

How far do you think you can **broad jump** from a standing position?
How high can you **jump** off the ground?
How far can you throw a **softball**?
How far can you **run** in 8 seconds?

	Estimate 1	Estimate 2	Actual	Difference
Broad Jump				
Vertical Jump				
Softball Throw				
8 Second Run				

Take students outside without any measuring devices and let them practice for a few minutes and then bring them back in and in the second column let them adjust their estimates. As a final step, take the students back to the playground with the various measuring devices and one by one let them perform the event and record the measurement. Upon returning to class, fill in column three.

Let students compare and discuss their estimates and actual performances.

Hands On, Inc
2121 Rebild Drive
Solvang, CA 93463

14	**Converts Standard Measures of Inches, Feet, and Yards into Equivalent Values**

Ruler Money

Grade Level: Middle/Upper

MATERIALS: Construction paper, markers, scissors, several yardsticks, and several rulers.

ORGANIZATION: Groups of four

PROCEDURE: This is an interesting crossover activity in which children work with a monetary system based upon linear measurements. It also gives students an opportunity to be creative in naming their newly created system. The purpose of this lesson is to solidify the concept of equivalencies of linear measurement.

Begin by displaying a ruler, yardstick, dollar bill, and a few coins. Ask students how these items are similar and elicit the statement that they both are used for measurement (although they measure different attributes).

Tell students that they are going to create a new money system based upon inches, feet, and yards and give students a few minutes to ask questions. Do not give away the equivalent measures, students should figure this out for themselves. Also tell students that they need to make up names for their money and then create the actual coins or dollars.

Many students will be familiar with the equivalent conversions but some students will need time to figure out that 12 inches equals one foot, 36 inches equals one yard, and that 3 feet equal one yard. They will also take time to decide upon names for their monetary amounts.

When they have created their monetary amounts, you might ask questions as to how they will write prices. Once general agreement is reached, you might have students create a catalog of prices for classroom items and let students team up to conduct sales transactions.

 Hands On, Inc
2121 Rebild Drive
Solvang, CA 93463

14	# Converts Standard Measures of Inches, Feet, and Yards into Equivalent Values

A Bird's Eye View of My House
Grade Level: Middle/Upper

MATERIALS: Graph paper, tape measure, and rulers

ORGANIZATION: Individually

PROCEDURE: This is an activity in which students will measure the perimeter of their houses and create a scale drawing. The conversion in this case will be 1' = the size of the graph paper, so it is a different type of conversion than those discussed in the three previous lessons.

The day before the lesson, assign students the task of measuring the perimeter of their houses. You might walk through this procedure with the class by measuring part of the school building. For those students who forget to do this, you might want to prepare one sample measurement to hand out to non-prepared students.

On the day of the activity, hand out graph paper and show students the concept of 1' = one edge of a graph square. Tell students that they will need to plan ahead to make certain they will have room on their paper. For students who have square or rectangular homes, extend the lesson by having them measure door and window openings to place on the drawing.

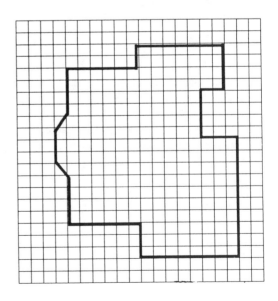

When finished, display the drawings. You will probably find a large discrepancy in the accuracy of the drawings. Many students have very little concept of creating this type of structured conversion.

Hands On, Inc
2121 Rebild Drive
Solvang, CA 93463

15	# Identifies and Measures the Parts of a Circle (Circumference, Arc, etc.)

Life as a Circle
Grade Level: Middle

MATERIALS: No special materials are needed for this activity

ORGANIZATION: A whole class activity

PROCEDURE: This is a beginning lesson in explaining the parts of a circle, and it can be used as a PE activity.

Divide the class into five groups -- circumference, diameter, radius, chord, arc. Ask students for input as to the meaning of each of these words. Use drawings to explain.

Next, take the students outside and begin by having the circumference group stand as a circumference (circle). Tell the diameter group to form a diameter in the circle, continue with the radius and chord.

Have the circumference group sit down and ask the arc group to form an arc and have the radius/chord/diameter groups try to form -- this can't be done.

Continue these types of activities having the circle become larger and smaller.

As a final activity, have students begin shifting positions -- "Arc become a diameter," "Diameter become a circumference," and "Radius become a chord." By going through the physical motions of forming these circle parts, students' recall will be greatly improved.

As an extension, you might assign a student to take measurements of the various parts of the circle which the students have formed. This can be easily done by using some long pieces of string and then measuring more closely when the class returns to the classroom.

Hands On, Inc
2121 Rebild Drive
Solvang, CA 93463

15	**Identifies and Measures the Parts of a Circle (Circumference, Arc, etc.)**

Bean Bag a Circle
Grade Level: Middle

MATERIALS: A bean bag, a circle area on the school playground

ORGANIZATION: A whole class activity

PROCEDURE: Students can do this activity as a PE experience, or it can be done during "math time."

Reinforce the vocabulary describing a circle, circumference, arc, chord, diameter, and radius. Be certain that students have an understanding of what these words mean. Take students out onto the playground and have them form a circle (circumference). Give the bean bag to one of the children and tell him to toss it to his "diameter (across the circle). At this point, the diameter and the chord are the only "tosses" available. Continue this process for a few minutes.

While the bag is being tossed, and while you are instructing "chord," "chord," "diameter," etc., suddenly say "radius." Since there is no one there, let the students solve the problem of how to provide a radius (select a student to stand in the middle).

Continue with the game including the new "radius" command. There are numerous variations which will occur to you and your children as the game progresses. Be creative and try some of your ideas.

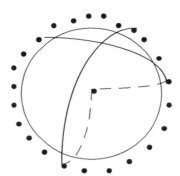

Hands On, Inc
2121 Rebild Drive
Solvang, CA 93463

15	**Identifies and Measures the Parts of a Circle (Circumference, Arc, etc.)**

Wheeling and Dealing
Grade Level: Upper

MATERIALS: Large pieces of cardboard; sticks; scissors; pins, nails, or screws; a tape measure; compasses

ORGANIZATION: Teams of three or four students

PROCEDURE: In this exercise, students will become familiar with the terminology of a circle by creating a measuring wheel. The teacher will want to make a model ahead of time to demonstrate the purpose of this wheel.

Review vocabulary involving a circle, circumference, diameter, radius, chord, and arc. Explain that students will be creating a measuring device to do "linear" measurements. Discuss why such a device is useful (measuring long distances, walking while you measure, avoiding the difficulty of rolling up a tape, etc.).

Tell students that there are several ways to complete this project. The teacher should demonstrate the assembly process but allow each group time to do problem solving to figure the measurement of the circumference. Allow freedom for students to choose the distance of measure (foot, meter, yard, etc.)

Some students will seek out the formula for circumference (C=pi x diameter), while others will experiment with measuring string and rolling the tape measure into a circle. This experimentation is the purpose of the lesson more than the finished product.

When students have finished, have a contest to see which group's measuring wheel is most accurate.

| 15 | **Identifies and Measures the Parts of a Circle (Circumference, Arc, etc.)** |

Bikes, Boards, and Skates
Grade Level: Upper

MATERIALS: Some type of wheel brought by each student (these might include bicycles, skateboards, roller skates, scooters)

ORGANIZATION: Individually or in teams of two students

PROCEDURE: This lesson will provide students an opportunity to experiment with measuring circumference, radius, and diameter. It is a basic lesson in the study of Pi.

On the day preceding the lesson, ask students to bring a "wheeled" vehicle to school the next day. Stress the need for variation to avoid every student bringing a bike or skateboard. You might even offer a prize for the most unusual entry.

On lesson day, have students complete a chart on which they show the measure of the wheel's radius, diameter, and then attempt to measure the circumference. Working in teams of two will make this more efficient.

Once students have made this measurement, write several samples on the board and discuss the ratio of radius to diameter to circumference. This ratio is pi.

Ask students to project how many times their wheel will turn in order to cover a given distance on the playground. Let them estimate (i.e. nine turns to cover the length of the volleyball court) and then let them do this experiment. Students should figure out how they are going to count the revolutions.

Once the experimentation is done, discuss the results with the class. By using vehicles which are close to the students, there will be a natural curiosity about how many times they need to pedal or push to cover a certain distance. This can lead into extensions on gear ratio, energy and physics and even into nutrition for providing this energy.

Hands On, Inc
2121 Rebild Drive
Solvang, CA 93463

16	Identifies Meaning of Milli, Centi, Deci, Hecto, Kilo, and Shows Equivalencies

Metrics Don't Bug Me!
Grade Level: Middle/Upper

MATERIALS: Markers, crayons, drawing paper, scissors

ORGANIZATION: Individually or as a whole class activity

PROCEDURE: This is an art lesson in which students create insects named with metric prefixes. Children will be familiar with a centipede and perhaps a millipede. Discuss the fact that centi means 100 in metric numbers, and because the centipede has so many legs it has been named accordingly.

Go over the various metric prefixes including: kilo, deci, centi, and milli and tell students that they are going to create insects which are named for these prefixes. They can use a variety of art forms such as cutting construction paper and pasting, drawing, coloring, etc.

Students should also complete a paragraph describing the unique habits of their "metrisect." All of these descriptions can be collated into a book for display.

There are numerous extensions including a metrisect mobile, drawings of metri-animals or metripeople, a student created filmstrip with voice describing the various bugs, and creative writing exercises describing a day in the life of their creation.

 Hands On, Inc
2121 Rebild Drive
Solvang, CA 93463

16	**Identifies Meaning of Milli, Centi, Deci, Hecto, Kilo, and Shows Equivalencies**

There's No Trick to Metric!
Grade Level: Middle/Upper

MATERIALS: Play money in one dollar, ten dollar, 100 dollar, and 1000 dollar bills; 10 dimes, 100 pennies for each group (Appendix A)

ORGANIZATION: Groups of four

PROCEDURE: This lesson provides an introduction to the metric system. It relates the money to the 10:1 ratio of the metric system.

Ask students to identify the various ways in which things are measured: length, weight, temperature, liquids, volume. Tell students that all of these measures can be done in metric and that unlike standard measures, metrics are all based on ten and use the same prefixes.

On the board, write: milli-centi-deci-
Meter
Gram
Square Meter   _____-deka-hecto-kilo
Liter

Discuss this information with the students and explain that our money system is in many ways like the metric system. The dollar is the basic component just as the meter/gram/liter are basic components of the metric system.

"deci" is equivalent to a dime
"centi" is equivalent to a cent
"milli" is equivalent to 1/10 of a cent
"deka" is equivalent to a $10.00 bill
"hecto" is equivalent to a $100.00 bill
"kilo" is equivalent to a $1000.00 bill

Once students see and understand the concept, have them measure various items and then relate the measurements to money values.. A brief list of suggested amounts includes:

1] Two kilograms ($2000); 2] 60 millimeters ($.60); 3] 25 dekagrams   ($250); 4] 15 hectoliters ($1500)

Once students understand the concept of this transfer, let them pose problems for one another within their groups. Providing this concrete example will help students solidify their understanding of the metric system.

Hands On, Inc
2121 Rebild Drive
Solvang, CA 93463

16	**Identifies Meaning of Milli, Centi, Deci, Hecto, Kilo, and Shows Equivalencies**

Different Ways with Days
Grade Level: Upper

MATERIALS: A calendar for each student that covers a ten year time period (<u>deca</u>de). A calendar is included in appendix e

ORGANIZATION: Teams of two students or individually

PROCEDURE: In this lesson, students will use the calendar as a means to work with the metric system. January 1 (of the 5th year) will represent the "midpoint," equivalent to the meter, gram, and liter. Students will move back in time to find the "equivalents of "deci," "centi," and "milli." They will move forward in time to find "deka," "hecto," and "kilo."

It may seem odd to compare metric prefixes to dates ,but the purpose is to show students that meter/gram/liter are central to the metric system, From these basic measurements the other metric prefixes make these "basics" either larger (kilo, hecto, deka) or smaller, fractional parts (milli, centi, deci).

A comparison can also be made to the concept of AD and BC as a chronological midpoint. Present students with the basic concept that "deci" = 1/10 of a meter/gram/liter and will be represented by a date 10 days before January 1. "Deka," on the other hand, is 10 times larger than meter/gram/liter and would therefore be represented by a date 10 days later. Students will have to create inventive ways of counting dates to move forward and backward 100 and 1000 days.

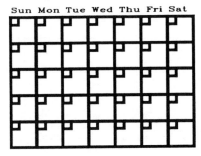 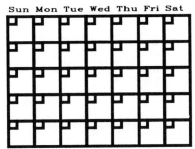 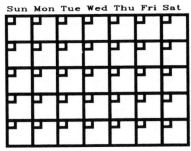

 Hands On, Inc
2121 Rebild Drive
Solvang, CA 93463

16	Identifies Meaning of Milli, Centi, Deci, Hecto, Kilo, and Shows Equivalencies

The Price is Metric!
Grade Level: Upper

MATERIALS: A catalog from a major department store (Sears, Montgomery Ward), Money (slips of paper) of seven colors

ORGANIZATION: Individually or in teams of two students

PROCEDURE: This is a simulation of the game show, The Price is Right, in which students "bid" on a catalog item in metric money. Their bids must be close to the real price of the item without going over the actual price. The catch is that they will bid in "metric money."

A suggested setup:
Red - Millidollars (1000th of a dollar - 1/10 of a cent)
Blue - Centidollars (1/100th of a dollar - 1 cent)
Yellow - Decidollars (1/10th of a dollar - 10 cents)
White - Dollars ($1.00 - equivalent to meter/liter/gram)
Green - Dekadollars ($10.00)
Orange - Hectodollars ($100.00)
Black - Kilodollars ($1000.00)

Begin by holding up the picture of an item (cover the price) and give students a few minutes to create a bid. Explain that they can't just say, "2,000 dollars." They must break it down into amounts such as, "Two kilodollars, one hectodollar, six dekadollars, three dollars, and eight decidollars." This amount would be equal to $2,163.80. In a short period of time, students will see the natural relation to the "decimal" system which we use to write money. The teacher should select a widely varied price range of items to be bid upon, with each team getting only one bid per item. As bids are made, they can be written on a chart similar to that shown.

Students will not use the the millidollars in their bids but they should still be provided to enhance their understanding of the metric system.

	Milli	Centi	Deci	Dollars	Deka	Hecto	Kilo
Team 1							
Team 2							
Team 3							
Team 4							

Hands On, Inc
2121 Rebild Drive
Solvang, CA 93463

17	**Differentiates Between Area and Perimeter**

Post and Stretch

Grade Level: Middle

MATERIALS: Geoboards and rubberbands for each student (or group) or graph paper, and a tally sheet

ORGANIZATION: Individually or in teams of two students.

PROCEDURE: Give each team a geoboard and ask them to place a rubber band around four "adjoining" posts (so that no posts are inside the figure).

Ask students to tell the perimeter for the figure they have created. They should arrive upon the measurement of 4 units.

Next, ask students to describe the number of "squares" they have created. (1 square unit).

Next, have students stretch the rubber band to cover two more posts and once again ask them to tell the perimeter (6 units) and the number of squares (2 squares). Ask students to continue with this procedure of adding two posts with each stretch and then writing the perimeter units and the square units on tally sheets.

Students will begin to experiment with stretching around posts and creating various shapes. As you circulate the room, ask students about the difficulties in finding the square units in these irregular shapes. Also ask how the perimeter changes when a diagonal line is created (lengthened).

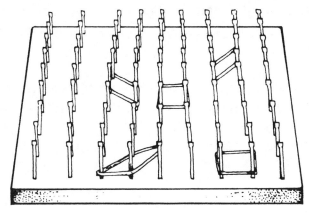

Hands On, Inc
2121 Rebild Drive
Solvang, CA 93463

17	**Differentiates Between Area and Perimeter**

Squarea

Grade Level: Middle

MATERIALS: Graph paper, scissors, glue for each student, various squares and rectangle cutouts which match graph paper lines.

ORGANIZATION: Teams of two, three, or four students.

PROCEDURE: Give each team a sheet of graph paper and a cutout of a square. Ask if they can find the area of the square. Many students will be uncertain of the concept of area so you will need to explain this.

Ask students to place the square on the graph paper and to trace around the edge — they should line it up with the graph lines. Once this is complete, they should have a drawing similar to the drawing below.

Ask student to count the number of squares that they have covered. Re-emphasize the point that these squares reperesent the "area" of the square. Hand out a rectangle shape and do the same procedure of letting students trace and then count the squares within the figure.

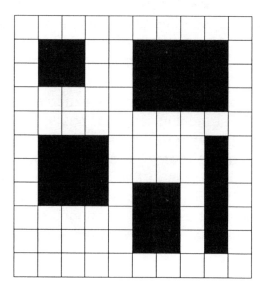

As students respond with answers of "9 squares" or "12 squares," emphasize the fact that the area of a figure is measured in "squares." To emphasize the difference between area and perimeter, you may have students count the distance around each shape.

Some students may be ready to move on to more complex shapes but as a beginning point we recommend that you stay with square and rectangular shapes.

 Hands On, Inc
2121 Rebild Drive
Solvang, CA 93463

17	**Differentiates Between Area and Perimeter**

What's in a Name?
Grade Level: Middle

MATERIALS: Block letter stencils or a computer program which prints banners, rulers, large sheets of paper

ORGANIZATION: Individually or in pairs (assisting one another with computation).

PROCEDURE: There are a variety of approaches to this activity. You may choose to have students plan and letter their names in block letters, you may choose to have them print out their names after learning to use one of the lettering computer programs, or you may have students use precut stencils to draw their names.

To simplify the activity you should ask students to square off rounded corners of letters such as "S," "P," etc.

Once students have generated a block lettering of their names, they will use a ruler to figure the perimeter and area of their names. You may wish to have students round off to the nearest inch, half inch, or quarter inch, depending upon their skills of computation. You might also use this lesson in conjunction with calculators to have students make the conversion from fractional numbers to decimal equivalents.

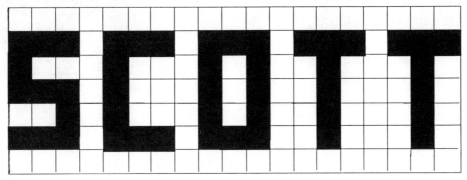

This activity can also be done using graph paper.

Hands On, Inc
2121 Rebild Drive
Solvang, CA 93463

17	# Differentiates Between Area and Perimeter

Leaf My Area Alone
Grade Level: Middle

MATERIALS: Leaves of various sizes and shapes although large leaves will work better than thin or narrow leaves, 1/2 inch graph paper

ORGANIZATION: Teams of three or four students

PROCEDURE: This activity can be tied in to a science unit on leaves. Have students walk around the school picking up three or four different leaves. You may wish to have them "press" leaves overnight in one of their books. They should use wax paper so as not to ruin book pages.

Have students trace their leaves on graph paper — 1/2 inch graph paper works well. Once leaves are traced, have each group decide upon the most efficient method to find the number of square units and the perimeter of each leaf tracing.

You may find that students will be more successful in their counting of square units if they cut out irregular shapes and glue them on colored construction paper. Matching of complementary shapes is easier to visualize if pieces are isolated and have a contrasting background.

Students should write a paragraph or explain their methodology to the entire class.

Hands On, Inc
2121 Rebild Drive
Solvang, CA 93463

18	**Determines and Uses Formulas to Measure the Area of Various Shapes**

The News is Not Black and White

Grade Level: Upper

MATERIALS: A newspaper section for each group, rulers

ORGANIZATION: Groups of four

PROCEDURE: Ask students to predict if there is more area of articles or of advertising in a typical newspaper section. They will be using the skills of figuring area to prove their hypotheses.

Let each group select a newspaper section. Remove the classified, comics, and movie sections from the possible choices.

Once students have selected a section, have them go through and measure the various heights and widths of articles/pictures and advertising and calculate the area. Since they are figuring numerous areas, they will have to rely on the base x height formula. You may want to create a miscellaneous category for areas of debate. There are a variety of approaches which groups will take in completing this task.

Extensions include comparisons of area for particular types of news stories and a study of the types of ads placed in various sections of a newspaper.

Hands On, Inc
2121 Rebild Drive
Solvang, CA 93463

| 18 | **Determines and Uses Formulas to Measure the Area of Various Shapes** |

Parallelograms Have Area Too
Grade Level: Upper

MATERIALS: Graph paper, scissors, paper, pencil, parallel cutouts

ORGANIZATION: Teams of two, three, or four students

PROCEDURE: The teacher should begin this lesson with discussion of the concept of a formula. It will help students to understand if you equate a formula to a recipe. By using the same ingredients and treating them the same way, a desired outcome is achieved. In this lesson, students will be "discovering" the formula (recipe) for the area of a parallelogram (they need not be familiar with this terminology).

Give each student a sheet of graph paper to use for tracing and measurement purposes. Have each student take a sheet of notebook paper (8 1/2" by 11") and fold it twice into a quarter of its original size. Take the quartered paper and trace its shape on the graph paper. Ask students to compute the area of the traced figure.

Discuss with students how they figured the area. Some will have counted squares while others will use B x H. Have students who used the formula explain how they know it works. Peer explanation will be much more effective than the teacher's. Try to focus students on using the terms "base" and "height" rather than "length" and "width."

Hand out parallelogram cutouts (prepared ahead of time) of various sizes to each student. Ask them to figure out the area of these shapes. Students will find this difficult (without rulers) due to the angular intersections on the graph paper. IMPORTANT - AT THIS POINT, TELL STUDENTS THAT TO FIND AREA OF A FIGURE, THEY MUST DISCOVER A WAY TO MAKE THE CORNERS SQUARE (RIGHT ANGLES). Using scissors, ask students to figure out a way to cut the parallelogram and make a rectangular figure. Allow time for experimentation but eventually one team member should discover the pattern as shown below. It does not really matter where they cut as long as it results in a rectangle.

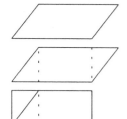

Ask if they have changed the shape of the parallelogram - yes; ask if they have changed the size of the parallelogram - no; Does the new figure now have square corners? - yes. By doing this, they have found the critical measurement of height. They can now figure the area by using graph paper.

To culminate the lesson, re-emphasize the concept that BASE times HEIGHT is the formula/recipe for the area of any parallelogram. Students can be given trapezoid cutouts to experiment with using the same procedure.

Hands On, Inc
2121 Rebild Drive
Solvang, CA 93463

18	**Determines and Uses Formulas to Measure the Area of Various Shapes**

Try This Angle For Size!

Grade Level: Upper

MATERIALS: Graph paper, scissors, an assortment of precut triangles, paper and pencil

ORGANIZATION: Groups of two, three, or four students

PROCEDURE: This lesson is an extension of the previous lesson which dealt with parallelograms. In this exercise students will discover the formula for finding the area of a triangle.

Begin by reviewing the purpose for formulas — to simplify and speed up computation. Have students take a sheet of notebook paper and fold it twice into quarter sections. Trace this shape onto the graph paper and have students compute the area. Students should be encouraged to recognize of base x height.

Ask students to use scissors and to cut diagonally across the quarter-folded sheet of notebook paper. Ask what shapes they have created (two triangles) and find a volunteer who is willing to tell the area of the triangle. Discuss with the class that the area of a triangle is always 1/2 the size of the square or rectangle it came from. Elicit a formula from the class (A = 1/2 B x H).

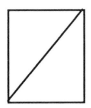

Hold up a triangle that was cut by a student (right triangle) and ask if anyone can think of a different type of triangle. Students will eventually come up with isosceles, scalene, and equilateral (although they may not know the terminology). Draw these triangles on the board (this over-simplification of triangle types may spark controversy since there is an overlap from one type to the next).

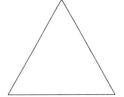

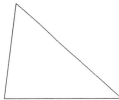

Hands On, Inc
2121 Rebild Drive
Solvang, CA 93463

Ask students to identify how the isosceles, scalene, and equilateral triangles you have drawn are different from the right triangle they cut out. The difference refers to the concept mentioned in the previous lesson, TO FIND THE AREA OF A FIGURE, YOU MUST REORGANIZE THE FIGURE SO IT HAS SQUARE CORNERS. How can the triangles on the board be restructured to become square figures? Refer students back to the statement made earlier — the area of a triangle is always 1/2 the size of the square (rectangle) it came from.

Hand out precut triangles to each student and let them try to make rectangles. To be successful they will have to trace the triangle on another sheet of paper and cut out the tracing. They will find that these two triangles make a parallelogram. The parallelogram can then be cut to make a square or rectangle. At this point, students have created a figure with square corners so they can now figure the area.

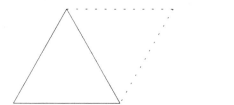 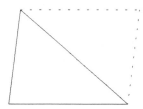

This is obviously the long way around to solve the problem, but students need to see this relationship. At this point students are ready to comprehend the critical attribute of finding the area of a triangle -- determination of the height.

Area = 1/2 B x H, and the height is the imaginary line that runs from the base to the top point of the triangle. Many of your students will make this discovery on their own, but with many you will have to work through the procedure of cutting, assembling, and manipulating the triangle shapes.

 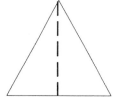 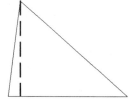

Students need this participation and manipulation if they are to understand why formulas work.

Hands On, Inc
2121 Rebild Drive
Solvang, CA 93463

19	**Develops an Understanding of the Meaning of "Pi" in Using Formulas to Find the Area and Circumference of a Circle**

Why Pi?
Grade Level: Upper

MATERIALS: Wastebasket, hula hoops, large rings, other large circle shapes, and string.

ORGANIZATION: Teams of three or four students.

PROCEDURE: One important concept for students to understand is what "pi" means. Before they can understand that the area of a circle is found by pi times radius squared or the circumference (perimeter) is pi times diameter, they must have the essential understanding of where "pi" comes from! This exercise will help them to discover why pi is 3.14.

Give each group a 6 to 10 foot piece of string and ask them to experiment with finding relationships within the "magical" circle shape. You may wish to discuss the vocabulary of radius, diameter, and circumference.

Eventually, students will find that the circumference is six times greater than the radius, approximately three times greater than the diameter, and that the diameter is twice the length of the radius. These are important relationships.

Explain that these ratios they discovered are the same for all circles. The ratio of circumference to diameter is so important it has a special name "pi;" it is usually written as 3.14, but this is a rounded off version of the number (Actually, pi divides as an irrational number with no even decimal equivlalent. Students can experiment with this by dividing 22 by 7).

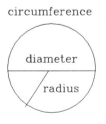

2 radius = 1 diameter

about 3 diameters = 1 circumference

▲
└── exactly is 3.14 or "pi"

Each time your class works with a formula involving pi, reinforce the concept of this ratio of 22:7.

19	**Develops an Understanding of the Meaning of "Pi" in Using Formulas to Find the Area and Circumference of a Circle**

Two Directions, Same Location
Grade Level: Upper

MATERIALS: An outdoor area with a large circle in chalk or paint.

ORGANIZATION: A whole class activity

PROCEDURE: Once students understand that pi is a ratio of the diameter of a circle to the circumference (see previous lesson), this activity will provide a tangible illustration of this ratio.

Discuss the concept of pi with the students and reaffirm that the 3.14 (or 22/7) tells us that the circumference of a circle is a bit more than three times the length of the diameter. Given this information, the students will be running a race in which student A will run the diameter and student B will run the circumference. Student A will have to run the diameter three times while student B makes one revolution.

Take the class outside and have them line up around the circle. Have them pair up with a student opposite them (across an imaginary diameter line).

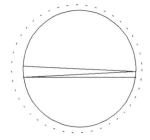

The teacher calls a student's name and says go. At the sound of go, the student whose name was called begins running (walking works effectively also) around the circle; the partner begins across-back-and across the circle. Both students will end the race at the same place.

You will find that if you run this race with all of your students that the number of winners for each "path" will be equal. Obviously, each race <u>should</u> end as a virtual tie but this rarely happens. Nevertheless, the concept of pi and its ratio will be remembered by your class.

Hands On, Inc
2121 Rebild Drive
Solvang, CA 93463

19	**Develops an Understanding of the Meaning of "Pi" in Using Formulas to Find the Area and Circumference of a Circle**

Square Squashing

Grade Level: Upper

MATERIALS: Construction paper, scissors, string or compass, rulers, glue

ORGANIZATION: Groups of three or four students

PROCEDURE: One of the most difficult aspects of math for teachers to explain is the use of formulas. Too often we tell children, "the formula is Area = pi x radius²" and we hope that students will remember this for years to come. Usually, this is not the case. In this lesson we have tried to give a concrete explanation of why this formula works.

Begin by telling your children that a circle is a unique shape and because it is unique it has several attributes all to itself, BUT a circle is really only a square without corners.

Students will know that they find the area of a square by multiplying s x s or base x height. To find the area of a circle, you do the same thing but the problem is that it has only one edge.

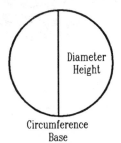

Tell students to imagine that a circle really does have a base and a height. Its height is its diameter, and its base is its circumference. Unfortunately, the diameter and the circumference are not the same as they are in a square, BUT they do have a set ratio or relationship; this ratio is called pi and it is the very thing that makes a circle unique!

The magical number is 3.14 or 22/7. This means that it takes a little over three diameters (or heights) to make a circumference.

Given this ratio, if we know the diameter (height) of a circle, we can find the circumference (base) by multiplying the diameter by 3.14. Once the students have obtained this number, it is simply a matter of multiplying base (circumference) times height (diameter) to find the area

To prove this to students, give them two small sheets of construction paper, a compass or string, a ruler, scissors, and glue. Have them draw a circle with the compass — it is best if they make a diameter of 2, 3, 4, or 5 inches.

Given the size of the diameter, have them figure the circumference (diameter x 3.14). In our drawings we will work with a circle with a 4" diameter.

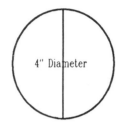

4 x 3.14 (pi) = Circumference, therefore 4" x 3.14 = 12.56"

The height of this circle is four inches. The base is 12.56 (roughly 12 and 1/2 inches). On the second piece of construction paper draw and cut out a rectangle which is 4" by 12 and 1/2".

Once this is done, cut up the circle and glue it onto the rectangle as shown.

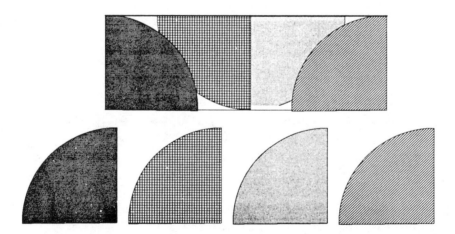

Although there are slivers of uncovered rectangle, there is also an overlap of circles. The concept that a circle is related to a square (or in this case a rectangle) will begin to surface.

As you continue to teach the concept of area of a circle, reinforce this concept of base times height. Students will realize that a circle is not foreign to the formulas they have already learned.

Hands On, Inc
2121 Rebild Drive
Solvang, CA 93463

20	**Computes Surface Area of Solids**

Another Side of the Story

Grade Level: Upper

MATERIALS: A variety of boxes, marking pens, construction paper, measuring devices

ORGANIZATION: Individually or in teams of two

PROCEDURE: This is a very basic lesson in the concept of surface area. Students will trace the six sides of a box onto construction paper, label the sides, and then compute the total surface area. The purpose of the lesson is to reinforce the concept that computing surface area requires students to work with ALL sides of a three dimensional figure.

Begin by handing out a box of some description (it should have a top to avoid any confusion). Students can bring boxes from home if necessary. Hand out construction paper and tell students that they will be figuring the surface area of their container.

Have them place the box on the construction paper and trace around the edges, when they have done this, have them label the figure as side, top, or bottom (you may want to have them number sides). Continue this procedure until all six surfaces have been traced and labelled. At this point discuss the similarities of the various shapes. Surprisingly, students will make some discoveries which we would expect them to already know, such as the height of all four sides is the same, and that there are three sets of identical shapes.

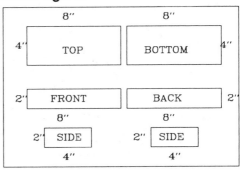

```
FRONT  = 16 SQUARE INCHES
BACK   = 16 SQUARE INCHES
SIDE   =  8 SQUARE INCHES
SIDE   =  8 SQUARE INCHES
TOP    = 32 SQUARE INCHES
BOTTOM = 32 SQUARE INCHES
```

SURFACE AREA = 112 SQUARE INCHES

Have them measure each of the shapes and compute the surface area. Remind them that they should be adding six numbers together when they finish finding the area of each tracing. Select a few of the students to review the procedure for finding surface area. Ask them to discuss if and how the surface area differs from the area of a figure.

Hands On, Inc
2121 Rebild Drive
Solvang, CA 93463

20	**Computes Surface Area of Solids**

A Square Deal

Grade Level: Upper

MATERIALS: Large pieces of graph paper, assorted boxes, tape or glue, and scissors

ORGANIZATION: Individually or in teams of two students

PROCEDURE: In this lesson, students will learn about surface area by covering a package with graph paper and counting the number of square units on the package.

Begin the lesson by discussing area, reinforcing the idea that area measures the number of "squares" in a two-dimensional figure. Explain that surface area is the same as area except that surface area measures the number of squares on all of the surfaces of a three dimensional figure.

Hold up a cube or box and ask students to describe the difference between the box and a square. Ask how many sides to the box and how many areas they will have to cover to measure the whole box. Continue this discussion until students have a firm understanding.

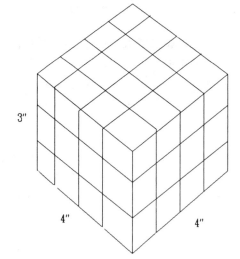

Hand out the materials to students and have them measure, cut, and glue graph paper to the boxes. Have them count the number of squares and write this number on each box side. Total the six sides and discuss the overall surface area.

The essential understanding that students need to grasp at this point is that area always describes flat surfaces and is always measured in square units.

Hands On, Inc
2121 Rebild Drive
Solvang, CA 93463

20	**Computes Surface Area of Solids**

Let the Truth Surface!

Grade Level: Upper

MATERIALS: A very large box (refrigerator or washing machine size) and 1" graph paper

ORGANIZATION: A small group or a whole class activity

PROCEDURE: This is a fun activity which involves group problem solving and coopera-
tion. Students should have some familiarity with finding surface area.

Ask students to estimate the number of square inches in the surface area of the large box. Write
their estimates on the board. Discuss various ways that they might make their guesses more
accurate (without measuring). Let them ponder some approaches to this estimation process.

Finally, tell students that they are going to measure
the box to see whose estimate is closest. At this point
give each student a single one inch square of one
inch graph paper and tell them that this is the measuring device. They will have to figure out a way to
measure the box by using one square per person.

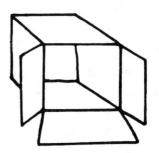

This activity can be a bit noisy, but the cooperative
aspect is worth the brief breakdown of decorum.

Hands On, Inc
2121 Rebild Drive
Solvang, CA 93463

20	**Computes Surface Area of Solids**

It Doesn't Get Bigger, It Gets BIGGER
Grade Level: Upper

MATERIALS: Graph paper, tape, scissors, tally sheets as shown

ORGANIZATION: Individually or in groups of two or three students

PROCEDURE: In this activity students will construct several cubes or rectangular prisms of various sizes and then complete a table showing probable sizes of larger containers.

Begin by having students imagine a small box of some type. The box may be 1 square by 1 by 1, 1 by 2 by 1, or any other variation. Then have them cut graph paper and tape their cuttings together to make the box. When they have finished with box 1, have them complete the information on the tally sheet.

Have them construct a second box which increases the size of the first box proportionally. A 1x1x1 would have to become a 4x4x4 to maintain a cube; a 1x2x1 would become a 2x4x2, etc. Have them construct this box and once again complete the tally sheet information.

	Top/Bottom	Front/Back	Side/Side	Surface Area
Figure 1				
Figure 2				
Figure 3				
Figure 4				
Figure 5				
Figure 6				

Construct a third box (9x9x9 and 3x6x3 would be the measurements of the samples) and complete the tally sheet. Given this information, have students project the size and surface area for the next three boxes (which they will not be making).

This concept will prove very useful as students move into more complex work with three dimensional figures.

Hands On, Inc
2121 Rebild Drive
Solvang, CA 93463

21	Identifies Ounces, Pounds, and Tons (Grams, Kilograms) as Standard Units of Measure and Uses Them to Estimate and Compare Weights of Various Objects

Tons of Fun

Grade Level: Middle

MATERIALS: Receptacles for collecting cans and newspapers, a bathroom scale

ORGANIZATION: A whole class project

PROCEDURE: This lesson presents students with the opportunity to learn first hand the weight of a ton. As a class project, students will be collecting newspapers and aluminum cans.

A ton of newspapers, while a large amount, is not an insurmountable amount to store in a classroom. The purpose of the aluminum can collection is to demonstrate that regardless of the material (paper or aluminum) a ton is still a ton but the volume of the material which makes a ton can be very different. Students will find that in the time it takes to collect one ton of papers, they will collect only a small amount (pounds) of cans.

It is fun for students to keep a tally of the weight of papers in pounds and kilograms as they collect them, and this reaffirms daily their awareness of the weight of a ton.

As an extension you might do a science unit on ecology and recycling. A study of the amount of newspapers, cans, bottles, and other trash which is thrown away each day is staggering to students.

	WEEK 1		WEEK 2		WEEK 3		WEEK 4		WEEK 5	
	CANS	PAPERS	CANS	PAPERS	CANS	PAPERS	CANS	PAPERS	CANS	PAPERS
MONDAY										
TUESDAY										
WEDNESDAY										
THURSDAY										
FRIDAY										

21	**Identifies Ounces, Pounds, and Tons (Grams, Kilograms) as Standard Units of Measure and Uses Them to Estimate and Compare Weights of Various Objects**

A New Way to Weigh
Grade Level: Middle

MATERIALS: A bathroom scale

ORGANIZATION: A whole class activity

PROCEDURE: This is an introductory lesson in which students will gain a concept of the size (weight) of a ton. Begin by asking students to guess the weight of an average elephant. Write responses on the board. Ask students if they have ever heard of a large measurement of weight other than a "pound." Many students will identify the ton.

Tell students that a ton is 2000 pounds, and ask if they think an elephant could weigh that much.

In today's activity students are going to see if the class weighs a ton. If you have students who are overweight you might choose to be discreet in weighing students individually. If students do not seem sensitive to being weighed, one by one have students come to the front of the room and record weights on the chalkboard, adding each weight in as you go. A second approach would be to weigh a few volunteers and generate a "student" average.

If your class is young or your class size small, you may not have 2000 pounds of children, in which case you might borrow some students from a neighboring classroom.

As a culminating activity, have each student color a picture of himself/herself and do a class collage with the title of "2000 pounds — Our Class Has a Ton of Fun!"

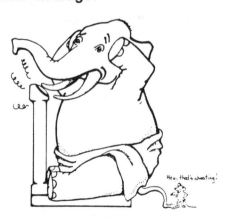

Hands On, Inc
2121 Rebild Drive
Solvang, CA 93463

21	Identifies Ounces, Pounds, and Tons (Grams, Kilograms) as Standard Units of Measure and Uses Them to Estimate and Compare Weights of Various Objects

A Real Light Weight

Grade Level: Middle

MATERIALS: Baggies, chips, popcorn, puffed wheat, cotton, packing material, balance scales, and other materials for estimating the weight of an ounce

ORGANIZATION: Groups of two, three or four students

PROCEDURE: This is an activity in estimating the weight of an ounce. Demonstrate this weight by handing out paper clips to each group and asking them the guess how many clips it would take to make an ounce (3 to 4 clips). You might also compare this to a gram which equals two paper clips.

Once they have this information as a guide, have them make a pile of chips, cotton, popcorn, packing material, paper, and other light objects to see how accurately they can estimate an ounce of each of these materials.

Have group members come forward and measure their estimates on the balance scale. You can extend this lesson to have students try to find the weight of one chip, one kernel of popcorn, one puffed wheat kernel, and one cotton ball. Based on their findings, have them estimate the number of these items it would take to equal their own weight.

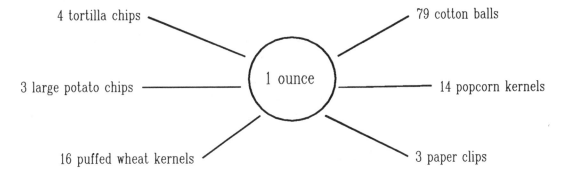

21	**Identifies Ounces, Pounds, and Tons (Grams, Kilograms) as Standard Units of Measure and Uses Them to Estimate and Compare Weights of Various Objects**

My Pop's a Kernel
Grade Level: Middle

MATERIALS: Popcorn (unpopped), popcorn poppers (have students bring air poppers from home if possible), balance scales or a kitchen scale

ORGANIZATION: Groups of four

PROCEDURE: This is an exercise in estimating weight and then measuring the difference in popped and unpopped popcorn.

Give each group a different amount of unpopped pocorn and have them weigh it. Make estimates within the group as to the weight of the popcorn after it is popped.

Decide beforehand what to do with each unpopped kernel. One approach is to count the number of unpopped kernels and to figure the relative weight of each kernel (i.e. one kernel = 1/35th of an ounce). The unpopped kernels can then be subtracted from the total weight of the popped corn.

Once popping has been done, have students compare the before and after weights. You might extend this to have students figure the weight loss (gain) per kernel in the popping process.

Unpopped kernels	Popped (with unpopped kernels removed)	Popped (with all unpopped kernels)
1 Ounce	3/4 ounce	7/8 ounce
3 Ounces	2 1/4 ounces	2 3/4 ounces
5 Ounces	3 7/8 ounces	4 1/5 ounces

Hands On, Inc
2121 Rebild Drive
Solvang, CA 93463

22	**Identifies Equivalencies of Weight Including Ounces, Pounds, and Tons (Grams and Kilograms)**

Separate but Equal

Grade Level: Middle

MATERIALS: Straws, paper clips, baggies, pins and string

ORGANIZATION: Individually or in teams of two students

PROCEDURE: Students will be making balance scales to measure ounces and equivalent weights.

The scale should be made as shown but students will need to realize that since the crosspiece is a straw, the weights measurable are very small. You might wish to extend this lesson to make a balance scale out of a large dowel. This lesson provides a means to introduce metric measurement of weight (grams) into the curriculum.

Let students experiment with their scales to find some equivalent weights — paper clips, pencils, and erasers are available and are light enough to use. After allowing some time for experimentation, let each group establish a base measure for comparison. This might be 8 paper clips, a particular pen, etc. They should then use this measurement to create an equivalent page of weights.

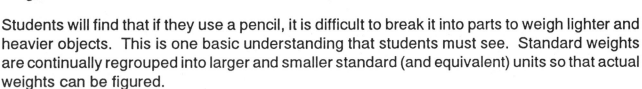

Students will find that if they use a pencil, it is difficult to break it into parts to weigh lighter and heavier objects. This is one basic understanding that students must see. Standard weights are continually regrouped into larger and smaller standard (and equivalent) units so that actual weights can be figured.

When students have realized this, they can begin to work with some of the metric weight measures (grams to kilos), as well as our standard measures of ounces to pounds. They should discuss why grams are a useful measurement.

Hands On, Inc
2121 Rebild Drive
Solvang, CA 93463

22	**Identifies Equivalencies of Weight Including Ounces, Pounds, and Tons (Grams and Kilograms)**

Adding Up the Ads
Grade Level: Middle

MATERIALS: Magazines, catalogs, advertisements, scissors, glue

ORGANIZATION: Groups of four

PROCEDURE: Have students search magazine advertisements for products which display weights and capacity in ounces. When items are found, students should cut them out and make a two part collage. Half of the the page should be items using ounces to measure liquid amounts; the other half should be items which measure their weights in ounces.

Taking this activity one step further you may want to do a "unit pricing" lesson similar to what students often see in a supermarket, that is, a price per ounce comparison.

Have students use the collage items and search through market advertisements to find prices of different size containers of the same product. Students can divide the price by the ounce size to generate a unit price list.

There are many other extensions possible including consumer price information, comparison of prices from one store to another, and cost per meal or per serving to name a few.

Brite Fabric Softener	6 oz.	12 oz.	36 oz.
Price	$1.81	$3.20	$6.35
Per ounce	$.30	$.27	$.18
Felix's Milk	32 oz.	64 oz.	128 oz.
Price	$.60	$.99	$1.97
Per ounce	$.018	$.015	$.015

Hands On, Inc
2121 Rebild Drive
Solvang, CA 93463

22	**Identifies Equivalencies of Weight Including Ounces, Pounds, and Tons (Grams and Kilograms)**

Canned Elephant?

Grade Level: Middle

MATERIALS: Assorted canned goods (brought from home), rulers, scale, calculators

ORGANIZATION: Teams of two, three, or four students

PROCEDURE: Students will use a can which they bring from home to do measurement of weight on a fulcrum. What makes the lesson interesting is that they must balance the weight of an average African elephant with the cans they have brought.

Obviously, they won't have enough cans so they will have to make computations from ounces to pounds to tons to see how many cans they would need to bring.

Begin by having students look at the cans they have brought. Some will be measured in fluid ounces, some in weight. Have each student weigh the can on a scale to obtain the actual weight.

Tell students that they are going to compute the number of cans it would take, stacked on top of one another to balance an elephant on the scale. Have the class look up elephants in the encyclopedia to determine an average weight.

Once they have figured the weight, have students figure out how many inches, feet, and yards (or meters) high the cans would stack.

If your students get really involved, you might have them figure out the volume of a box which would hold a given number of cans — to do this, they will have to take the cylinder shape and imagine a box that would enclose one can and then multiply that figure.

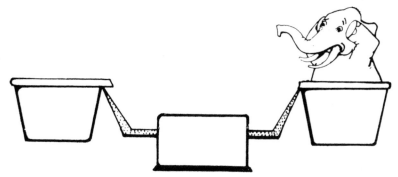

22	**Identifies Equivalencies of Weight Including Ounces, Pounds, and Tons (Grams and Kilograms)**

A Not So Auto-Mobile

Grade Level: Middle

MATERIALS: Coat hanger for each student, string, scissors, a balance scale, objects weighing one pound

ORGANIZATION: Individually or in teams of two

PROCEDURE: Students will be creating a mobile which demonstrates that 16 ounces equals a pound.

Most students will have created a mobile, explain that in this particular mobile there are going to be two equal sides: a one pound side and a 16 ounce side. Using a measuring device such as a balance scale or a kitchen scale have students find an object which weighs a pound.

Next, have the students search the room and the playground for objects which weight one ounce. Ideally, they will need 16 objects.

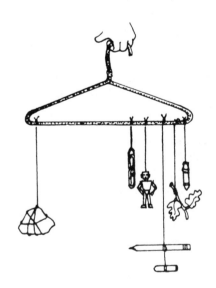

Give each group time to assemble the mobile, placing the pound object on one end and the ounce objects on the other. Upon completion display the mobiles in class to provide a visual reminder of the ounce-pound equivalency.

Hands On, Inc
2121 Rebild Drive
Solvang, CA 93463

23	**Identifies the Properties of a Cube and Constructs Shapes Using Cubes**

A Cube Is a Cube Is a Cube
Grade Level: Middle

MATERIALS: Construction paper, glue, scissors, an assortment of cubes (sugar cubes, toy blocks, unifix cubes, etc.)

ORGANIZATION: Teams of two students

PROCEDURE: This is a very basic lesson in which students will begin to identify the properties of a cube, first by observing, and then making cubes.

Hold up the various cubes you have collected and ask students to tell why a cube is a cube. They should identify that the base, height, and depth are all the same (this vocabulary should be used); that the surface is made up of six squares of equal size; and that the figure is three dimensional (rather than two dimensional).

Once this discussion has occurred, hand out construction paper, scissors, tape and glue and let each team try to make a "family" of cubes (various sizes). This activity will take time and patience, but it is an important step for children to learn about the "structure" of a cube.

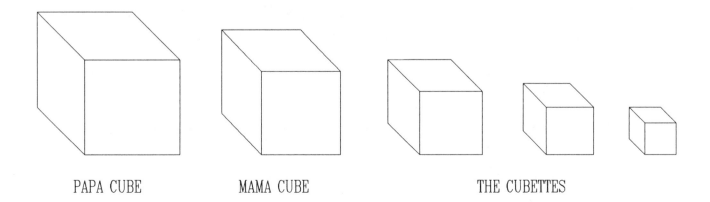

PAPA CUBE   MAMA CUBE   THE CUBETTES

Hands On, Inc
2121 Rebild Drive
Solvang, CA 93463

23	**Identifies the Properties of a Cube and Constructs Shapes Using Cubes**

Our Lives Take Shape
Grade Level: Middle

MATERIALS: Tally sheet as shown

ORGANIZATION: Teams of three or four students

PROCEDURE: This is a lesson in observation in which students will be searching for similar two and three dimensional shapes: squares and cubes, rectangles and rectangular prisms, circles and spheres or cylinders.

Give each group a tally sheet and let them spend a few minutes perusing the room, writing down the various objects in the room in the proper category. After a few minutes, discuss the findings of the students as a class.

You will probably need to clarify the concept with many students that the side of a cabinet may be a rectangle but the cabinet is a rectangular prism.

As a homework assignment, have students search their homes and complete a list of 5 to 10 items in each category. Ask students to be creative in finding these shapes.

	SQUARE	RECTANGLE	CIRCLE	CIRCLE
TWO DIMENSIONAL SHAPES				
THREE DIMENSIONAL SHAPES	CUBE	RECTANGULAR PRISM	CYLINDER	SPHERE

Hands On, Inc
2121 Rebild Drive
Solvang, CA 93463

23	**Identifies the Properties of a Cube and Constructs Shapes Using Cubes**

The Last Straw, Revisited
Grade Level: Middle

MATERIALS: Straws, string, scissors

ORGANIZATION: Groups of two, three, or four students

PROCEDURE: Give each student five or six straws and have him cut each straw to 5 inch lengths. Thread each string through straws to create a cube. Give students the opportunity to struggle with the procedure. When they successfully make a cube, they will have a much better understanding of the sides and structure of this three dimensional shape.

Using the straw cube as a model, ask students questions about the cube. Terms including base, height, width, depth should be used. Next, discuss the concept of volume and surface area. Surface area is an abstraction in this case in that there are no sides to the student's cube.

You might have students cover the exterior of the straw cube with graph paper to provide a more concrete example of surface area.

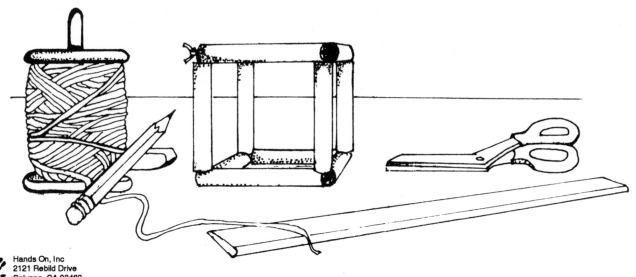

23	Identifies the Properties of a Cube and Constructs Shapes Using Cubes

Pick a Square
Grade Level: Middle

MATERIALS: Flat toothpicks, glue (quick drying)

ORGANIZATION: Individually or in teams of two

PROCEDURE: Students will learn about the cube shape by building a model from toothpicks.

Give each student 24 toothpicks. Tell the class that they are going to make several squares and then combine these squares to make a cube. It is important that as they glue toothpicks together, they intersect near the tip of the toothpicks. If students are careless about this, the cube will be off center and will not glue together.

As students are working, circulate and ask questions such as, "How many squares will you have to make in order to create a cube?" How is the cube shape going to be different than the square shape?"

Emphasize the concept of three dimensions with the students. The "hands-on" creation of these two shapes will help solidify the differences between two and three dimensions.

As an extension, you might have your class create other two and three dimensional shapes such as a triangular pyramid or a rectangular prism. Many students will also be interested in the geodesic dome concept in architecture.

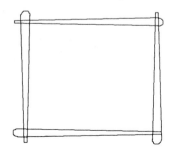 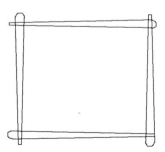

Hands On, Inc
2121 Rebild Drive
Solvang, CA 93463

24	**Counts Number of Cubic Units in a Given Figure and Constructs Figures to Find Specific Volume**

Blockozoid

Grade Level: Middle

MATERIALS: Spinners (Appendix A), and cubes (sugar, unifix, etc.)

ORGANIZATION: Groups of three students

PROCEDURE: Students will use spinners to determine the base, height, and width of shapes and then construct these shapes.

Have students make spinners with six sections, numbered from 1-6. Player 1 will spin the spinner and this will be the base of the figure. The student should construct this part of the figure. Player 2 spins and constructs the height of the figure. Player 3 spins and constructs the depth of the figure.

Once the figure is constructed, students can count the number of cubes in the figure. Let them discover that by multiplying the base x height x depth they can find the volume without counting cubes.

Also reinforce that the volume is made up of cubes and therefore the volume must be labelled "cubic units."

Player 1
BASE
Spins 3

Player 2
HEIGHT
Spins 4

Player 3
DEPTH
Spins 5

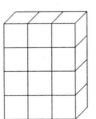
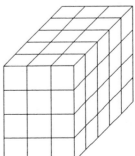

Hands On, Inc
2121 Rebild Drive
Solvang, CA 93463

24	**Counts Number of Cubic Units in a Given Figure and Constructs Figures to Find Specific Volume**

Another Side of the Story

Grade Level: Middle

MATERIALS: Graph paper, rulers, five cubes (sugar, unifix, blocks)

ORGANIZATION: Teams of two or three students

PROCEDURE: In this activity, students will be given five cubes and will construct a shape. They can lay them out or stack them but they must be touching one another completely on one side.

Once a shape has been created, students will do drawings of the shapes from all six sides. By moving their positions and counting cubes, they will be able to view the shape from five sides (front, back, top, side, side) but will have to visualize the shape from the bottom. Students should label each view on their drawings.

Once the drawings have been completed, they should disassemble the cube structure and give the drawing to classmates to see if they can reconstruct the figure.

There are numerous extensions to this activity. You might give students more cubes to work with, have them create the shape against a corner of the room so they can see only three sides, or play a puzzle game in which students do a drawing from three sides and a classmate must try to complete the drawings from the remaining three sides.

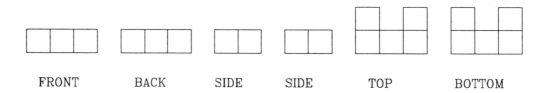

FRONT   BACK   SIDE   SIDE   TOP   BOTTOM

Hands On, Inc
2121 Rebild Drive
Solvang, CA 93463

24	# Counts Number of Cubic Units in a Given Figure and Constructs Figures to Find Specific Volume

Cube It!

Grade Level: Middle

MATERIALS: Sugar or unifix cubes, dice

ORGANIZATION: Groups of two students

PROCEDURE: This is a game activity which gives students practice with the terminolgy of height, depth, and width.

Begin the explanation of the game by giving each group 27 sugar cubes and one die. Each player takes 13 cubes. The object of the game is to use your 13 cubes to build a larger cube before your opponent uses his 13 cubes. The die will be used to tell whether to add a cube to the height, the depth, or the width of the 3 by 3 by 3 cube you will be creating.

If students roll a 1 or 2, they must add to the height of the cube. If they roll a 3 or 4, the depth is added; if a 5 or 6 is rolled, a width cube is added. There are two "rules" 1) whenever a cube is added, it must touch at least <u>one edge of another cube</u>; 2) all cubes are added <u>in relation to the "starter cube."</u> That is, depth must be played BEHIND an existing cube, height must be placed ON TOP of an existing cube (second and third rows), and width must be placed ALONG SIDE an existing cube.

Should the student roll a number which will not allow a play, he loses his turn and the opponent gets to roll. The student who uses all of the cubes first is the winner.

Starter Cube   Player 1 Rolls "2" (Height)   Player 2 Rolls "6" (Width)   Player 1 Rolls "3" (Depth)

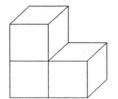
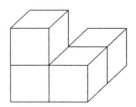

24	**Counts Number of Cubic Units in a Given Figure and Constructs Figures to Find Specific Volume**

Architects in the Making

Grade Level: Middle

MATERIALS: Rulers, graph paper, cubes (sugar, unifix, etc.)

ORGANIZATION: Individually

PROCEDURE: Drafting skills are being taught less and less in schools; this activity is merely a superficial introduction into this field, but the process of drawing a top, side, and front view of a figure is so beneficial to the concept of volume that we have included it here. As a teaching aid, you might want to find a copy of a drafting textbook, because you will undoubtedly find that several of your students become very interested in this activity.

Give each student a set of 4 to 10 cubes and have them arrange them into a shape of some type. Given this shape have them construct a drawing (similar to that pictured below) with a top, side, and front view. Using graph paper will make this activity much easier for the student, but as they become more proficient, you may wish to let them use plain paper and get the added practice of drawing to scale.

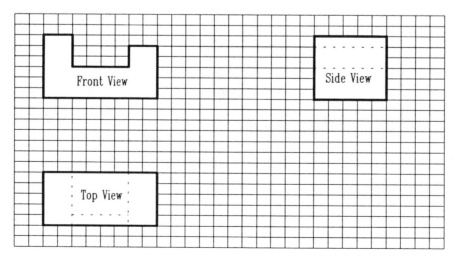

Hands On, Inc
2121 Rebild Drive
Solvang, CA 93463

25	**Differentiates Between Surface Area and Volume**

Squares Outside, Cubes Inside
Grade Level: Upper

MATERIALS: One inch cubes, one inch graph paper, tape

ORGANIZATION: Groups of four

PROCEDURE: In this activity, students will be comparing the surface area of a figure they have created to the volume of that same figure. They will do this by physically making a shape from the graph paper and then filling this shape with cubes.

Give each group several sheets of graph paper and several cubes (20-30).

Have each group member make a three dimensional shape such as a cube or rectangular prisms Use graph paper and tape to make the shapes (they will have to leave one side open), but have them make the top anyway so they can measure it and have a clearer grasp of the concept.

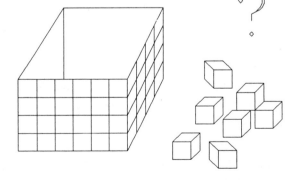

Once the shapes are complete, have them compute the surface area of the figure they have created. Let them fill the container with cubes to find the volume. Emphasize the fact that surface area is measured in SQUARE UNITS and volume is measured in CUBIC UNITS.

When all students have completed this task, have them chart the information and prepare to An extension could be to use an ice cube tray and sand instead of cubes. They can count the number of "sand cubes" it takes to fill the container. This method will also allow students to discover the cubic volume of areas of irregular shapes.

Hands On, Inc
2121 Rebild Drive
Solvang, CA 93463

25	**Differentiates Between Surface Area and Volume**

Moo Juice Magic

Grade Level: Upper

MATERIALS: Milk cartons cut to open-topped cubes, scissors,

ORGANIZATION: Teams of two, three, or four students

PROCEDURE: Discuss the difference between 2 and 3 dimensional figures. Have students draw various 2 and 3-D figures.

Hold up a milk carton and ask students whether it is two or three dimensional. Ask if there is a way for them to make a milk carton into a two-dimensional figure. Have students cut the carton and lay it flat on the desk.

With the carton flattened out, ask students to tell the area and perimeter of the carton but remind students that the top side is missing.. Emphasize the proper labeling of inches and square inches in their answers.

Relate this information to volume by re-forming a cube and asking students if the contents of the cube could be measured in linear or square units. The point to be made is that linear and square units are two dimensional and cubic units are three-dimensional.

Depending upon the understanding of students, discuss various means of figuring cubic units. Since cubic units are three dimensional, students must learn that they have to multiply three numbers together

Hands On, Inc
2121 Rebild Drive
Solvang, CA 93463

25	Differentiates Between Surface Area and Volume

Will the Ratio Please Surface?

Grade Level: Upper

MATERIALS: Construction paper, scissors, masking tape

ORGANIZATION: Groups of three or four students

PROCEDURE: In this activity, students will attempt to prove whether or not there is a relationship between the surface area of a figure and its volume.

Each group should work with a different shape — rectangular prism, cube, triangular prism, pyramid, and cylinder. You may need to spend some time reviewing the various formulas with each group. Each group member should select a different size model to construct and then find the volume and surface area of his model.

Once all students have figured these measurements, have the group decide if there is a relationship or ratio between the volume and the surface area.

Have each group prepare a report for the class to present their findings.

Base	Height	Depth	Surface Area	Volume
1	2	1	10 square units	2 cubic units
2	4	2	30 square units	16 cubic units
3	6	6	90 square units	54 cubic units

25	**Differentiates Between Surface Area and Volume**

Sixtominoes

Grade Level: Upper

MATERIALS: Large graph paper (1" or 3"), scissors, tape, rulers

ORGANIZATION: Groups of four

PROCEDURE: This is a puzzle type activty in which students will cut out shapes of six square units and see whether or not it can be folded to form a cube. We call the new shape a sixtomino.

Hold up samples as shown below. Sample A is a sixtomino (it can be folded, without cutting, into a cube). Sample B is NOT a sixtomino because it cannot be folded into a cube.

Given this information, have each group try to create 5 shapes which are and 5 shapes which are not sixtominoes. Students will need several sheets of graph paper but encourage groups to think or visualize rather than immediately cutting.

Once the templates have been cut, ask students to list 3 things which all sixtominoes have in common and 3 things which non-sixtominoes have in common.

Sample A   Sample B

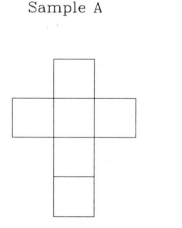 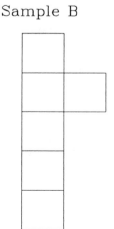

26	Computes and Identifies Properties and Formulas to Determine the Volume of Various Three Dimensional Shapes

What You See Is Wrong!
Grade Level: Upper

MATERIALS: A sheet of paper for each student, scotch tape, rice or small beans

ORGANIZATION: To be done individually or in teams of two students

PROCEDURE: In this lesson, students will be working with an optical illusion of sorts but in the process will learn about the relationship of surface area to volume.

Give each student a sheet of construction paper (approximately 8" by 11") and ask students to measure the paper and figure the area. Next, have them roll it into a cylinder. Some students will roll it lengthwise and some will roll it by width (this is acceptable) and tape the rolled edge together.

Ask students to speculate if the tall cylinder and the wide cylinder will have the same volume. Mark their responses on the chalkboard.

Have students pair up in teams of unlike cylinders and measure the amount of rice that will pour into the tall cylinder; then measure the amount of rice that will pour into the wide cylinder. They will find an amazing discrepancy. Give students time to hypothesize as to why this is true. Remind them that the area of the construction paper (surface area) is the same.

Eventually students will notice that the top and bottom of the cylinder are of different sizes and therefore the overall surface area is different. Have students compute the actual surface area and volume of both cylinders by using the formulas: $A = pi \times R^2$; $A = C \times H$; $V = pi \times R^2 \times H$

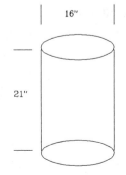

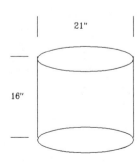

Hands On, Inc
2121 Rebild Drive
Solvang, CA 93463

26	Computes and identifies properties and formulas to determine the volume of various three dimensional shapes

Clay Play

Grade Level: Upper

MATERIALS: Modeling clay, knives or ice cream sticks (to cut clay)

ORGANIZATION: Individually or in teams of two or three students

PROCEDURE: This can be categorized as an exploration activity in which students create various three dimensional shapes and then cut the shapes in various ways to discover more about formulas.

Basic volume formulas which you may want to include:
    cube = S x S x S or S³
    rectangular prism = L x W x H
    pyramid = L x W x H divided by 3

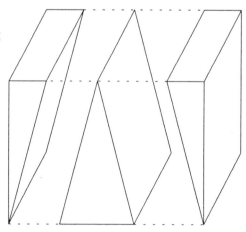

Visualization of the pyramid shape is the ultimate goal. Have your students begin by making a cube or a rectangular prism. The figure shown is only the first step in cutting the pyramid shape. The formula for this figure would be L x W x H divided by 2. When the other two sides have been removed students will see why it should be divided by 3.

Once they have models of a cube or prism, have them experiment with cutting off various sides to make pyramids. You will find that many students will have real difficulty with figuring out what and where to cut but the nice thing about clay is that it can be reformed and they can try again. It is important that students create pyramid and triangle shapes by cutting rather than forming these shapes. They need to see the pieces that are "cut off" in order to visualize why the formulas work.

As a final step, have each student select a favorite shape and prepare a short presentation as to why the formula for this shape makes sense. It doesn't have to be a pyramid. It can be a shape that has been created by the students as long as they relate the formula back to a cube or rectangular prism.

Hands On, Inc
2121 Rebild Drive
Solvang, CA 93463

| 26 | Computes and Identifies Properties and Formulas to Determine the Volume of Various Three Dimensional Shapes |

Just One Thin Dime

Grade Level: Upper

MATERIALS: Rolls of pennies, nickels, dimes, and quarters, rulers measuring to the 1/16th of an inch, calculators

ORGANIZATION: Groups of four

PROCEDURE: Rather than using real money for this activity you may want to use play money coins which are readily available in five and dime stores. The "real money" aspect gets students more involved.

In this lesson, students will be using the formula for the volume of a cylinder to assign a monetary value to cubic units of pennies, nickels, dimes, quarters, and half dollars. It provides a high interest approach to finding volume.

Begin by reviewing the formula for finding the volume of a cylinder (pi x radius²x height). You may need to review the concept of pi (see task analysis 29). Give students a couple of sample problems to do by drawing cylinders on the board or overhead. Also mention the labeling of cubic units. One final point, since students will be working with fractions from the ruler, you may want to have them use 22/7 for pi. An alternative is to use a calculator to convert fractions to decimals.

Ask students if they would prefer to have a 3" stack of dimes or a 3" stack of quarters and ask why? How can they prove this? Ask if they would rather have a cubic foot of dimes or of quarters. Ask why? How can they prove this? This is the basis of the lesson.

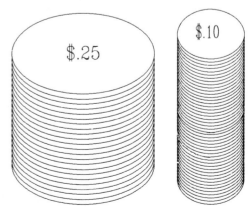

The money should circulate from one group to the next. Give pennies to group 1, dimes to group 2, etc. after calculations have been completed, have the rolls rotate to the next group.

(Over)

Hands On, Inc
2121 Rebild Drive
Solvang, CA 93463

Have students make a 1, 2, or 3 inch stack of coins (this will be the height). They should then measure the diameter of the coin and cut this figure in half for the radius. Compute the volume. Total the value of the coins in the stack and divide the volume by the value. This is the value of a cubic inch of that coin. Complete the table.

We have done this activity for you but our figures may differ since we carry out decimals only two or three places.

	Diameter	Radius	# of Coins to Inch	Pi x R² x H	Value of 1" stack	Value divided by Volume gives the total value per cubic inch
Penny	.75"	.38"	17	.453 cu. in.	$.38	$.84 per cu. inch
Nickel	.81"	.41"	13	.529 cu. in.	$.65	$1.23 per cu. inch
Dime	.69"	.35"	19	.386 cu. in	$1.90	$4.92 per cu. inch
Quarter	.94"	.47"	12	.694 cu. in.	$3.00	$4.32 per cu inch

Students will find that a cubic inch of dimes has a greater value than a cubic inch of quarters. It is important to point out that these figures do not represent any "space" between coins. As an extension, you might want to have students perform the experiment to see if dimes continue to be more valuable if coins are stacked in the same size container.

 Hands On, Inc
2121 Rebild Drive
Solvang, CA 93463

40	**Estimates the Size of Various Containers and Measures Equivalent Units Among Cups, Pints, Quarts, and Gallons (Liters, Milliliters)**

One for the Birds
Grade Level: Middle/Upper

MATERIALS: A large bag of birdseed, rice, or beans; a large (five gallon or bigger) tub; various measuring cups (ounce, cup, pint, quart, gallon) for each group

ORGANIZATION: Groups of four, five, or six

PROCEDURE: Students will be experimenting with estimation of container size and equivalence. Give each team an assortment of measuring cups. If you want to add an extra element to this lesson, they can actually create their own measuring cups from milk cartons.

Circulate around the room pouring a large amount of seed (rice or beans) into each group's large container. Pour enough so they will have to do some measuring in gallons. As they look at this large supply of seed, have them estimate — how many gallons of seed are there? How many quarts? How many pints? How many cups? How many ounces? Have them write their estimates on a sheet of paper.

Next, give each group time to figure a means of determining the liquid measure of the seed. There are several approaches which students can take. Allow them to experiment.

Once students have an understanding of relative size, play an estimation game within each group. Have one student be the "estimator" and the other group members the "checkers." Pose a problem such as, "without measuring, pour three ounces of birdseed into the quart container." Let the estimator do this and have checkers review the accuracy of the estimation.

The ultimate goal of this lesson is to allow students to physically handle the various sized containers and to use them in a problem solving situation.

Hands On, Inc
2121 Rebild Drive
Solvang, CA 93463

40	**Estimates the Size of Various Containers and Measures Equivalent Units Among Cups, Pints, Quarts, and Gallons (Liters, Milliliters)**

Contain Yourself
Grade Level: Middle/Upper

MATERIALS: Various liquid containers brought by students; ounce, cup, pint, quart, and gallon measures, access to water

ORGANIZATION: To be done individually

PROCEDURE: This is an introductory exercise in estimation of liquid measurement. On the day preceding the lesson, ask students to bring a number of liquid containers to school — preferably empty. These might include food, detergent, cosmetic, beverage, or garage type containers which hold liquids (warn them that some liquids are dangerous and they should check with parents).

This is an exploratory activity and depending upon the sophistication of your class may take several days to complete.

Once containers have been acquired, display five of various size and ask the class to estimate the capacity of each container. These estimates might be in ounces, cups, pints, quarts, or gallons. Undoubtedly, many students will have no concept of these measurements.

As the teacher you will need to make a decision as to where to set your objective. Concept 2 should be to estimate the relationship of ounces to cups/pints/quarts/gallons etc. Concept 3 should be to select the appropriate measuring unit for a given container. For example, it would not be appropriate to estimate the capacity of a five gallon container in ounces or cups, just as it would be inappropriate to measure a three ounce container as a fractional part of a gallon. Concept 4 should be the actual conversion from one measure to the next.

Once you have discussed the concepts with the students, take the class outside and let them begin experimenting with relative size by pouring water from one container into another and measuring the relative sizes.

Hands On, Inc
2121 Rebild Drive
Solvang, CA 93463

40	**Estimates the Size of Various Containers and Measures Equivalent Units Among Cups, Pints, Quarts, and Gallons (Liters, Milliliters)**

A Slinky Cylinder

Grade Level: Middle/Upper

MATERIALS: A garden hose, measuring cups (quart and gallon), access to water

ORGANIZATION: A whole class activity

PROCEDURE: This lesson can be approached in two ways — as a fun experience in estimating liquid capacity, or as a sophisticated lesson in which students estimate capacity of various hoses — differing in diameter and length.

Begin by asking students to estimate how many ounces of water a 50 foot garden hose would hold it if were completely full. Discuss different ways of reaching a reasonable estimate.

After discussing this, let the class create a method of filling a hose on the school playground. You can use this time as a brainstorming session. They should also create a method of measuring the amount of water in the hose once it is filled.

Take the class outside and fill and measure the contents of the hose. If your students are working at a basic level of understanding, you can return to the classroom to do some conversion of gallons to quarts to pints to ounces. If your class is more sophisticated, challenge them to measure the length and diameter of the hose and then to project the amount of water that would be contained in 1/2, 5/8, or 3/4 inch hoses of varying lengths.

An interesting extra could be to have students figure the surface area of these various hose diameters and length.

Hands On, Inc
2121 Rebild Drive
Solvang, CA 93463

| 40 | Estimates the Size of Various Containers and Measures Equivalent Units Among Cups, Pints, Quarts, and Gallons (Liters, Milliliters) |

Dis-place-ment a Lot to Me

Grade Level: Upper

MATERIALS: Large container (5 gallon) for water, balloons, a waterproof marking pen

ORGANIZATION: A whole class activity

PROCEDURE: ~In this activity, students will be estimating the size of an ounce, cup, pint, quart, and gallon of air by doing a displacement measurement in a tub of water. The purpose is to provide a tangible method of estimating liquid measurement.

Begin by explaining displacement and measurement. In this case, our method of measurement will be to fill a container (one quart at a time) marking the water level with each additional quart. You might choose to have students do this same process by filling a styrofoam cup ounce by ounce and marking each increase as a first step in explaining the process.

When marks are made to the top of the cup (or large container), pour out one or two ounces of water — this will allow students to measure displacement.

With marks in place and containers filled, give each student a balloon and have them blow it up to an estimated one ounce capacity — measure by submerging it in water and marking the higher water level. Try a two ounce size, then cup size, pint size, quart size, and gallon size as you move from the styrofoam cups to the large container.

The effort involved in setting up the lesson may seem extreme, but students are practicing many important measurement skills in preparing to do this displacement activity.

Hands On, Inc
2121 Rebild Drive
Solvang, CA 93463

40	**Estimates the Size of Various Containers and Measures Equivalent Units Among Cups, Pints, Quarts, and Gallons (Liters, Milliliters)**

The Sands of Time

Grade Level: Upper

MATERIALS: Sand, various containers, (one liter soft drink bottles work well), washers, timers, stopwatches

ORGANIZATION: Individually

PROCEDURE: In this activity many measurement elements are brought together. Students will be creating an hourglass to count out a specific amount of time. This may be 1 minute, 1 hour, or 1 day, the student may decide.

We recommend that you do this project in two phases. First, let all students create an hourglass using sand or water (directions below), and then have students create a new and unique hourglass at home as a week-end project.

One of the easiest ways to create an hourglass is to use two large plastic soft drink containers. If you cut the top off of one container and keep the cap on the other, you can insert the capped container into the cut thus creating an hourglass shape.

The cap can be punctured so liquid or sand can drip (pour) through or you can put washers over the ends of the bottles to restrict the flow.

Let students experiment with this arrangement, and for this experimentation you might cut the bottom off of the capped container to create a funnel. In this way, students can pour one ounce, one cup, one quart, or whatever measurement into the top without disassembling the hourglass. As they experiment, they should time the drip process and create a formula such as one ounce = 10 seconds, one cup = 80 seconds, one quart = 320 seconds. They should experiment to see if equivalent amounts of liquid measures create equal amounts of time.

Once you have created this interest in time and liquid measure, move to phase two of the process and have students create a new and different type of hourglass at home.

Hands On, Inc
2121 Rebild Drive
Solvang, CA 93463

40	**Estimates the Size of Various Containers and Measures Equivalent Units Among Cups, Pints, Quarts, and Gallons (Liters, Milliliters)**

More for Your Money

Grade Level: Upper

MATERIALS: Full cups of beverages (small, medium and large) from various fast food restaurants, measuring containers

ORGANIZATION: Groups of four

PROCEDURE: Students will enjoy this activity, which shows the price per ounce of soft drinks at various fast food restaurants. It does take some coordination to get all of the drinks at school at the same time, but with the help of two or three parent volunteers, students will learn a lot about liquid measurement.

It is helpful to have a separate, small, medium, and large beverage for each group. It is even more interesting if each group has a sample from a different restaurant.

Give each group three containers (for melting ice) and a measuring cup. As soon as beverages arrive at school, have students spoon the ice from the beverage into separate containers (keep the small, medium and large ice separate as well).

While the ice is melting, measure the amount of beverage in each cup and record amounts on a chart. When the ice has melted, measure the ice amount and record the answer. Once the measurement has been done, have students compute the price per ounce for beverage, and the price per ounce for ice (water) and beverage together. Have each group prepare a short presentation as to whether the small, medium, or large is the best deal.

$.082 per oz. $.065 per oz. $.041 per oz.

Do a class comparison as to which fast food restaurant provides "the most for your money."

Hands On, Inc
2121 Rebild Drive
Solvang, CA 93463

110

Making a Spinner

Many activities in this book require the use of spinners. Students can make their own spinners very easily and inexpensively by following the directions given here.

Materials required are: cardboard, scissors, compasses, rulers, pencils, **paper clips, a paper** punch, and tape.

1. Cut out a cardboard (tagboard) pointer and punch a hole in the center.

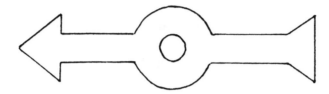

2. Cut a scrap of cardboard as a paper washer and punch a hole in the center.

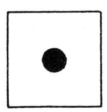

3. Cut out a four inch square of cardboard and divide it into quarters as shown. **Make light pencil** lines.

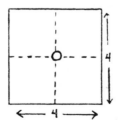

4. At the center of the square, make a small hole with your paper clip.

5. Using a compass, make a circle on the four inch square and draw a design you wish to use. You may wish to color your spinner at this point.

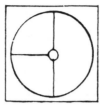

6. Bend the center loop of the paper clip up at a 90 degree angle to the outer loop.

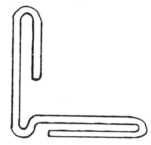

7. Tape the outer loop of the paper clip to the bottom of the four inch square to hold it in place.

8. Put the bent paper clip through the hole in the four inch square, the paper washer and the pointer.

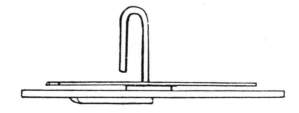

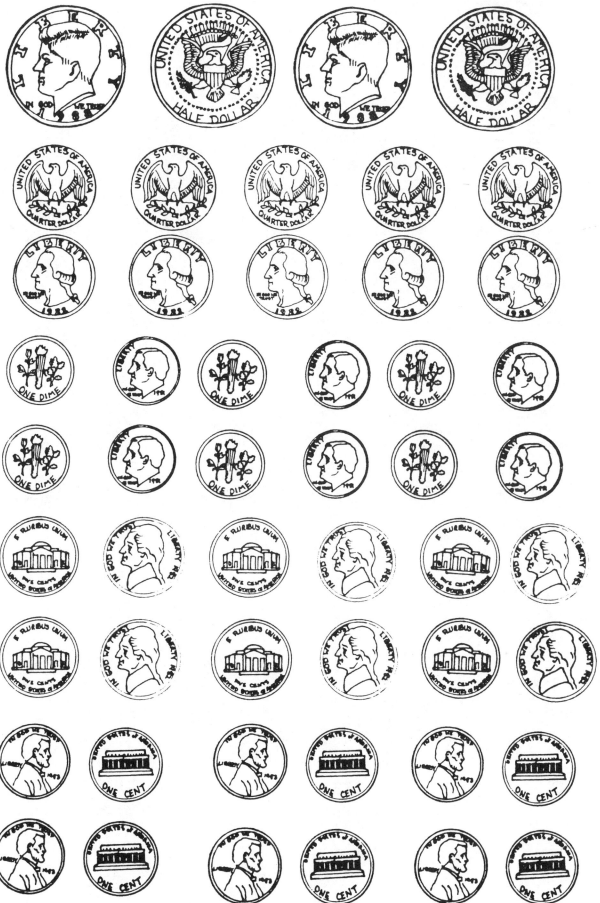

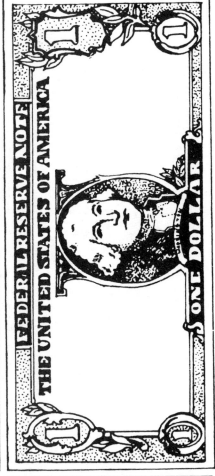

H	A	N	D	O
		FREE SPACE		

Equivalency Cards

1 **10 CENTS** $.10	10 **5 CENTS** $.05	19 **95 CENTS** $.95
2 **20 CENTS** $.20	11 **15 CENTS** $.15	20 **8 CENTS** $.08
3 **30 CENTS** $.30	12 **25 CENTS** $.25	21 **11 CENTS** $.11
4 **40 CENTS** $.40	13 **35 CENTS** $.35	22 **16 CENTS** $.16
5 **50 CENTS** $.50	14 **45 CENTS** $.45	23 **19 CENTS** $.19
6 **60 CENTS** $.60	15 **55 CENTS** $.55	24 **22 CENTS** $.22
7 **70 CENTS** $.70	16 **65 CENTS** $.65	25 **31 CENTS** $.31
8 **80 CENTS** $.80	17 **75 CENTS** $.75	26 **37 CENTS** $.37
9 **90 CENTS** $.90	18 **85 CENTS** $.85	27 **42 CENTS** $.42

Equivalency Cards

1	10	19
2	11	20
3	12	21
4	13	22
5	14	23
6	15	24
7	16	25
8	17	26
9	18	27

Perpetual Calendar

1821	2	1847	6	1873	4	1899	1	1925	5	1951	2	1977	7	2003	4	2029	2	2055				
1822	3	1848	14	1874	5	1900	2	1926	6	1952	10	1978	1	2004	12	2030	3	2056	14			
1823	4	1849	2	1875	6	1901	3	1927	7	1953	5	1979	2	2005	7	2031	4	2057	7			
1824	12	1850	3	1876	14	1902	4	1928	8	1954	6	1980	10	2006	1	2032	12	2058	1			
1825	7	1851	4	1877	2	1903	5	1929	3	1955	7	1981	5	2007	2	2033	7	2059	2			
1826	1	1852	12	1878	3	1904	13	1930	4	1956	8	1982	6	2008	10	2034	1	2060	10			
1827	2	1853	7	1879	4	1905	1	1931	5	1957	3	1983	7	2009	5	2035	2	2061	5			
1828	10	1854	1	1880	12	1906	2	1932	13	1958	4	1984	8	2010	6	2036	10	2062	6			
1829	5	1855	2	1881	7	1907	3	1933	1	1959	5	1985	3	2011	7	2037	5	2063	7			
1830	6	1856	10	1882	1	1908	11	1934	2	1960	13	1986	4	2012	8	2038	6	2064	8			
1831	7	1857	5	1883	2	1909	6	1935	3	1961	1	1987	5	2013	3	2039	7	2065	3			
1832	8	1858	6	1884	10	1910	7	1936	11	1962	2	1988	13	2014	4	2040	8	2066	4			
1833	3	1859	7	1885	5	1911	1	1937	6	1963	3	1989	1	2015	5	2041	3	2067	5			
1834	4	1860	8	1886	6	1912	9	1938	7	1964	11	1990	2	2016	13	2042	4	2068	13			
1835	5	1861	3	1887	7	1913	4	1939	1	1965	6	1991	3	2017	1	2043	5	2069	1			
1836	13	1862	4	1888	8	1914	5	1940	9	1966	7	1992	11	2018	2	2044	13	2070	2			
1837	1	1863	5	1889	3	1915	6	1941	4	1967	1	1993	6	2019	3	2045	1	2071	3			
1838	2	1864	13	1890	4	1916	14	1942	5	1968	9	1994	7	2020	11	2046	2	2072	11			
1839	3	1865	1	1891	5	1917	2	1943	6	1969	4	1995	1	2021	6	2047	3	2073	6			
1840	11	1866	2	1892	13	1918	3	1944	14	1970	5	1996	9	2022	7	2048	11	2074	7			
1841	6	1867	3	1893	1	1919	4	1945	2	1971	6	1997	4	2023	1	2049	6	2075	1			
1842	7	1868	11	1894	2	1920	12	1946	3	1972	14	1998	5	2024	9	2050	7	2076	9			
1843	1	1869	6	1895	3	1921	7	1947	4	1973	2	1999	6	2025	4	2051	1	2077	4			
1844	9	1870	7	1896	11	1922	1	1948	12	1974	3	2000	14	2026	5	2052	9	2078	5			
1845	4	1871	1	1897	6	1923	2	1949	7	1975	4	2001	2	2027	6	2053	4	2079	6			
1846	5	1872	9	1898	7	1924	10	1950	1	1976	12	2002	3	2028	14	2054	5	2080	1			

The following are calendar grids numbered 1 through 14, each showing the twelve months (January–December) with day-of-week layouts. Calendars 3, 4, and 5 are additionally labeled with the years 1985, 1986, and 1987 respectively.

Calendar 1 — JANUARY, MAY, SEPTEMBER, FEBRUARY, JUNE, OCTOBER, MARCH, JULY, NOVEMBER, APRIL, AUGUST, DECEMBER

Calendar 2 — JANUARY, MAY, SEPTEMBER, FEBRUARY, JUNE, OCTOBER, MARCH, JULY, NOVEMBER, APRIL, AUGUST, DECEMBER

Calendar 3 — 1985 — JANUARY, MAY, SEPTEMBER, FEBRUARY, JUNE, OCTOBER, MARCH, JULY, NOVEMBER, APRIL, AUGUST, DECEMBER

Calendar 4 — 1986 — JANUARY, MAY, SEPTEMBER, FEBRUARY, JUNE, OCTOBER, MARCH, JULY, NOVEMBER, APRIL, AUGUST, DECEMBER

Calendar 5 — 1987 — JANUARY, MAY, SEPTEMBER, FEBRUARY, JUNE, OCTOBER, MARCH, JULY, NOVEMBER, APRIL, AUGUST, DECEMBER

Calendar 6 — JANUARY, MAY, SEPTEMBER, FEBRUARY, JUNE, OCTOBER, MARCH, JULY, NOVEMBER, APRIL, AUGUST, DECEMBER

Calendar 7 — JANUARY, MAY, SEPTEMBER, FEBRUARY, JUNE, OCTOBER, MARCH, JULY, NOVEMBER, APRIL, AUGUST, DECEMBER

Calendar 8 — JANUARY, MAY, SEPTEMBER, FEBRUARY, JUNE, OCTOBER, MARCH, JULY, NOVEMBER, APRIL, AUGUST, DECEMBER

Calendar 9 — JANUARY, MAY, SEPTEMBER, FEBRUARY, JUNE, OCTOBER, MARCH, JULY, NOVEMBER, APRIL, AUGUST, DECEMBER

Calendar 10 — JANUARY, MAY, SEPTEMBER, FEBRUARY, JUNE, OCTOBER, MARCH, JULY, NOVEMBER, APRIL, AUGUST, DECEMBER

Calendar 11 — JANUARY, MAY, SEPTEMBER, FEBRUARY, JUNE, OCTOBER, MARCH, JULY, NOVEMBER, APRIL, AUGUST, DECEMBER

Calendar 12 — JANUARY, MAY, SEPTEMBER, FEBRUARY, JUNE, OCTOBER, MARCH, JULY, NOVEMBER, APRIL, AUGUST, DECEMBER

Calendar 13 — JANUARY, MAY, SEPTEMBER, FEBRUARY, JUNE, OCTOBER, MARCH, JULY, NOVEMBER, APRIL, AUGUST, DECEMBER

Calendar 14 — JANUARY, MAY, SEPTEMBER, FEBRUARY, JUNE, OCTOBER, MARCH, JULY, NOVEMBER, APRIL, AUGUST, DECEMBER

Each calendar month grid uses the column headers: S M T W T F S

Sun	Mon	Tue	Wed	Thu	Fri	Sat

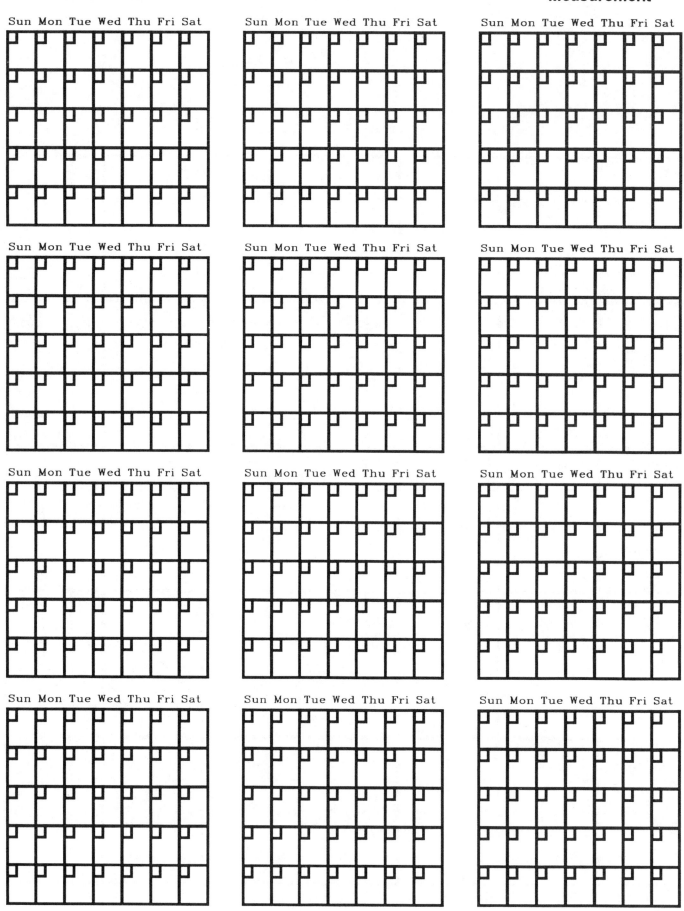

MOTOCROSS

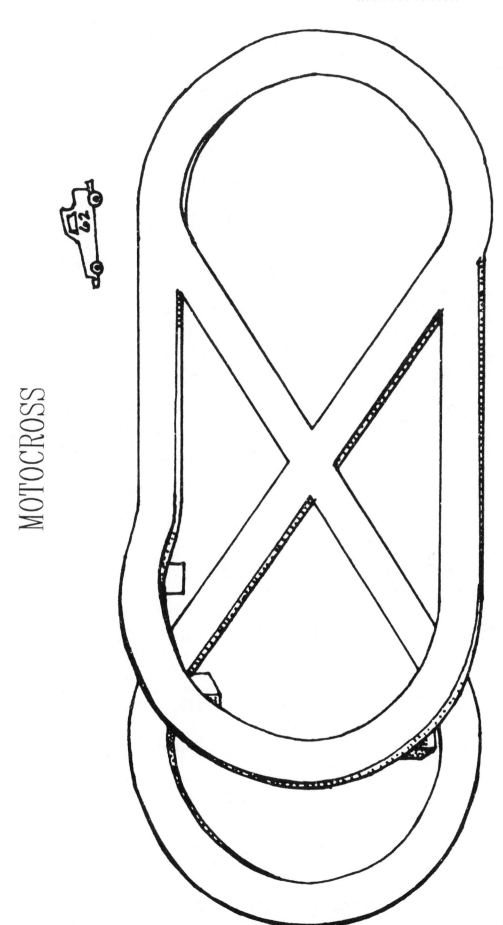

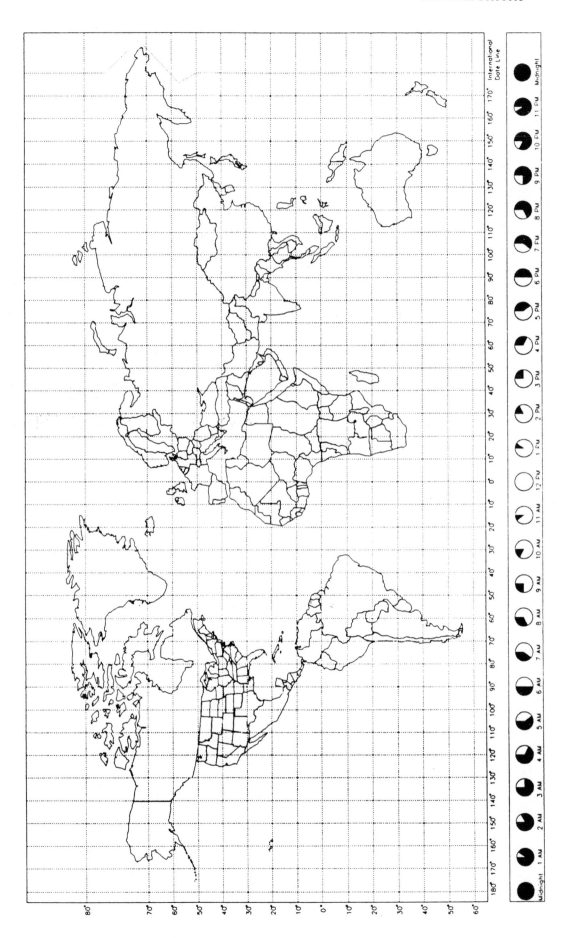